CW00665597

My Thousand and One Cars

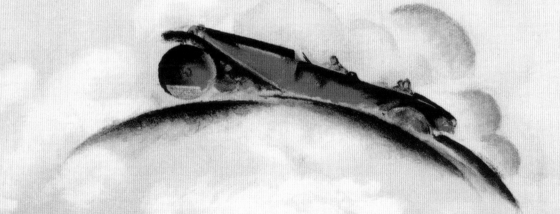

VOISIN

AUTOMOBILES

Translated by D.R.A. Winstone
with the permission of La Table Ronde

Designed by West End Studios
Printed in the UK by EuroPrint

Cover illustration adapted from a 1922 lithograph by Jean Barrez (Joe Bridge)
Frontispiece adapted from a 1923 lithograph by Charles Loupot
Sketch of Gabriel Voisin by Antoine Protopazzi in 1930

First published in France in 1962
as *Mes mille et une voitures*

Published by Faustroll
All rights reserved © 2012
ISBN: 978-0-9569811-2-7

www.faustroll.co.uk

CONTENTS

Foreword		6
Introduction	Scandal, bureaucracy and the end of aircraft manufacture (1913-18)	11
Chapter I	1913-18: scandal, bureaucracy and the end of aircraft manufacture	21
Chapter II	1900-19: the first cars, post-war diversification and the 4-litre	41
Chapter III	1922-1925: coachwork, hillclimbs and the C5	73
Chapter IV	1922: belief and temptation	95
Chapter V	Knight engines, the Blue Train and Bernard's small fours and sixes	105
Chapter VI	The 'boom', bearings and design approach	124
Chapter VII	The 1922 Strasbourg GP, the Routes Pavées scandal and the 33CV	140
Chapter VIII	1923-24: the Tours and Lyon GPs and questions of balance	161
Chapter IX	1927-31: record breaking at Montlhéry and the 17CV	177
Chapter X	The thirties: V12s, the Aérosport, the FWD V8 and the Belgians	191
Chapter XI	The Voisin dockyard, the lozenge car, the C30 and Aéromécanique	215
Chapter XII	The war years: steam, pedal power and political treachery	227
Chapter XIII	The fifties: SNECMA, Biscooters, Spain and the 1EP	233
Appendix I	On safety, traffic and weight	263
Appendix II	Notes on modern car design	282
Postscript	The patents of Gabriel Voisin	288

FOREWORD

Gabriel Voisin was in his eighties when he dictated this second volume of his autobiography, which was published without the benefit of an editor. It is therefore best appreciated as a series of discursive reminiscences rather than a conventional chronological account.

The annotations in this reference edition are intended to fill some of the gaps that this inevitably entailed, because Voisin, notwithstanding a justifiable pride in his own contribution to the two defining technologies of the twentieth century, was a man who famously always looked forwards rather than to the past. This may well account for the many omissions from these recollections of a long and prolifically productive life.

The translation attempts to capture the flavour of his distinctive prosody, a quirky mix of what can now sometimes seem somewhat stilted *fin de siècle* Edwardian syntax with the bluff directness of a man who always wore his blue mechanic's overalls with pride.

What emerges is the self-portrait of a robustly opinionated character, at times intemperately dismissive of those he considered fools, and at others disarmingly tender (with friends of both sexes). A practical man who couldn't look at a functional object without trying to devise a better way of fulfilling its purpose. A man with no head for business, but who worked as hard as he played. A man unmotivated by money, but who spent it with panache. Politically unclassifiable, culturally conservative yet perpetually critical of the status quo. In some ways sentimental, in others not at all. Unafraid of self-deprecation. Drily witty, too.

Autocratic he may have been, like so many larger-than-life characters of his ilk, but clearly also charismatic enough to inspire fierce loyalty. This was wholly reciprocated; when Voisin refers to his collaborators as spiritual sons, he means just that. Such powerful emotional bonds as are hinted at in this text play a significant and often ignored part in the transmission of ideas.

More generally, Voisin's account is revealing because, like Ettore Bugatti, he exemplified that last generation of manufacturers who were truly *auteurs* of the products that bore their name. In a collective endeavour as multi-faceted as the motor industry, it could be hard even at the time to quantify the influence of any individual. By contrast, every single component of a factory-bodied Voisin bears the stamp of its creator's thinking just as surely as if it were signed.

Gabriel Voisin was not one of the world's great car makers (although he did make some great cars). Ultimately, his work in everything but the early aviation years left little lasting impression apart from the profound influence he undoubtedly had on the design approach of André Lefebvre, and all that implies. But, like a pebble skimming a lake, everywhere he made contact, he radiated ripples of unconventional thinking: bold, original and, in an essentially French way, rational. And peripheral as it may be, that's the provocative and prolific contribution he made to the evolution of the motor car..

My Thousand and One Cars
by Gabriel Voisin

Reference Edition

Translated and annotated by D.R.A.Winstone

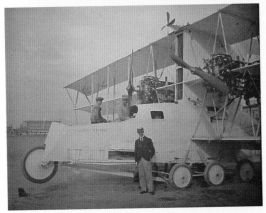

Variants of the Voisin 13.5 metre light bomber were manufactured in large numbers, by Breguet and Michelin as well as Voisin in France and in several countries abroad. GV is seen centre left (in boater) in 1915, dwarfed by the firm's giant 38m experimental triplane.

Introduction,
by way of an interlude

The gods being in agreement, I shall perhaps finish this book. It follows a first volume, *Mes dix mille cerfs volants*,[1] in which I related my life from 1880, when I was born, to 1918. I also wanted to share a few observations that my peers in the motoring world are well aware of but often ignore, so that these fundamental principles won't have to await the end of the great transport revolution in order to be 'rediscovered'.

Before committing it to paper, Anatole France[2] once told me the tale of a boy who, dying of boredom, accepted from a fairy a magic bobbin of golden thread - the thread of his days. To overcome life's difficult moments, all the child had to do was pull the sparkling yarn, and time would pass in the blink of an eye.

The fairy vanished, and the sorcerer's apprentice duly unwound the thread until he reached adolescence. Enchanted, he then transformed himself into a young man, and suddenly finding himself in love, cut short with a single gesture the time separating him from the union he so dearly desired. So unbearable did he find the wait for a first child that he drew on the magic thread yet again. Worries, sickness, the grief of bereavement, all were pretexts for unravelling the golden yarn from its spool. By the time death snatched him away, our hero had actually lived just two months, ten days and a few minutes.

---

1) First published in 1961 (English translation *Men, Women and 10,000 Kites*, Putnam 1963)

2) GV had known the popular novelist and Nobel laureate since the writer Michel Corday introduced them to each other (along with GV's future wife) at the Reims air meeting in 1909. An enthusiast for things mechanical even in his 70s, France replaced his ancient Panhard with a new 4-litre Voisin in 1920. He was even driven to his grave in one.

Not having met this fairy myself, I never held the weft of my life in my hands. But were I deprived of the ordinary ways of measuring the passage of time, my life would seem little more than a frantic succession of ephemeral dreams. It was nevertheless full of unpredictable events, sorrows and joys, of crowning passions peppered with 100,000 pipedreams and resounding failures, all of them tossed in the raging torrent that still bears me headlong toward the jaws of death…

Before the First World War, on the eve of the President of the Republic's decision to order our industry colleagues to build Voisin aeroplanes, I had at my disposal a factory in which a hundred or so friends worked with a degree of courage, faith and selflessness which still astonishes me.

I neglected the administration of my company, and we lived in perpetual financial difficulties, constantly embarking on costly experiments which were not in those days funded by the state as they are now. Innocent as we were of the tricks of the research trade, the construction, materials, testing and development of our prototypes were entirely at our own expense.

By the end of 1915, after a year of hostilities, the Voisin company had expanded with alarming speed. I employed 2,000 people, and five aircraft a day left our hangars, whose doors opened directly onto the *champ de manoeuvres*[3] at Issy-les-Moulineaux, by then converted into an aerodrome.

---

3) The former cavalry training ground alongside which the hangar was built in 1907 for Henri Farman's Voisin biplane, and on which he flew the world's first officially observed closed circuit kilometre in January 1908. It soon became the cradle of France's aeronautical industry. Today, the Paris heliport still occupies part of the area.

Like a gigantic machine, the company functioned more or less adequately, but one of my worries concerned the personnel. Since August 1914 I had wielded a dangerous power: the ability to order the recall of named individuals from the Front. At my whim, a soldier could turn his back on the terrors, privations and perils of the front line, and after proving his skills, take his place in our factory.

Once it became known, this possibility unleashed an avalanche of letters. Supplicants inundated our mailbag and I was bombarded with importunate demands from parents, friends, nobodies and 'people of influence'. The flower in the rifle[4] had long since been forgotten…

I did my best to resist, but was soon obliged to surround myself by a department specifically to handle this question of recalls and resign myself to the irregularities that inevitably ensued.

Tired of seeing our works and offices staffed by the useless, the idle and the cack-handed, whose numbers rapidly grew to scandalous proportions, I decided to call a halt to such recalls and instead handed over lists of the specialists we needed to the military authorities. This decision did not have the effect I expected. Terrified by the prospect of investigation, those who sought cushy sinecures thought up ingenious ways to keep out of sight. Rumours began circulating throughout the company. The quality of our products was brought into question, and the suggested remedy was implemented on the spot.

A veritable army of so-called military 'inspectors' unconnected with the official Aviation Construction Service insinuated themselves into the factory, but by the time this ploy

4) A reference to the assurances given to infantrymen in 1914 that France's overwhelming military superiority would guarantee easy victory within weeks.

came to my attention it was too late to take action. Things that required no supervision whatsoever were being minutely checked and verified, and the consequent delivery delays began to be problematic. Useless, expensive encumbrances as they were, these 'inspectors' had at all costs to justify their existence. One inspection followed another until this tomfoolery eventually led to the unexpected absurdity of re-inspecting entire aeroplanes immediately after their final inspections.

The quality standards to which we worked were such that these repeated inspections were in themselves of no real concern. But such machinations, although outside our organisation proper, nevertheless gave rise to innumerable problems.

Immediately after the victory of the Marne,[5] we had on military orders opened a reserve factory in Lyon, which functioned perfectly well. The director was Rivierre. This branch was of course systematically and unscrupulously exploited by those seeking cushy jobs with their innumerable checks, inspections, rubber stamps and double-checks. Supplemented by legions of female secretaries, they lost no time in hobbling the rhythm of our work to the point that the complaints from the front line became more and more pressing.

The drama of Verdun[6] exasperated these parasites, whose interference had finally become intolerable. One day in the Lyon branch, a hapless fitter whose conscription had been deferred made an insignificant error in making some non-critical component. This man, like those around him, was immediately haunted by the spectre of a return to the Front.

5) September 1914 - a victory in which GV claimed that reconnaissance from Voisin aircraft played a critical role.

6) February-December 1916.

He falsified the stamp on the components in question with a poorly made tool, and, having been denounced by some wretch, the 'authorities' chose this occasion to make a dramatic example of the incident: the management of my Lyon branch, including Rivierre, were promptly put under lock and key.

An official telegram insisted on my presence at the scene of the crime. The local press doubled its circulation by squealing "Combatants Betrayed by Rear Guard" and other such promising headlines which I read for myself on my arrival at Lyon.

The Aviation Construction Service was fortunately represented in Lyon by honest men. Although the affair in question was sorted out in a couple hours, the memory of the 'faked stamps' affair remained the No.1 concern of our parasitical inspectors and those they inspected. Weary of constantly battling against hostile inquisitions from within the organisation itself, in a moment of ill temper I decided to close my company down.[7]

Within three days, a buyer presented himself – a fairly unpleasant big business type, but who offered me eight million francs for the Voisin factories.[8] The size of this sum (equivalent to about a billion 1961 francs) astonished me. The Issy-les-Moulineaux notary, who had never dreamed of such a godsend, expedited the sale.

---

7) Although the atmosphere GV describes no doubt contributed to his decision, he had also been informed by the military on February 5th 1917 that no more large orders for Voisin bombers would be forthcoming (on the grounds that the machines were outmoded), and that he would therefore be required within five months to convert the Voisin factories for the manufacture and assembly of Hispano-Suiza engines. Proud as he was, a profitable sale must have seemed a more attractive option to GV than the humiliation of subcontracting. He had also been hurt by personal criticisms in the wake of a spate of spontaneous engine fires.

8) The company was sold on August 18th 1917 to the Lyon-based Établissements Charles Lefebvre at a declared price of 7 million FF in a transaction of labyrinthine complexity involving three elements: 3.55 million francs for the two factories in the rue Gambetta and rue Jean-Jacques Rousseau, together with 1600m^2 of land GV had acquired since 1914; a separate 'added value' lease on the neighbouring land; and in a third transaction, the factories' tooling, materials and stock, whose value appeared as 2.65 million francs on the books, but was invoiced to the military for an additional 4 million francs.

Ten days after my decision, I was a free man.

I then built a research laboratory, asked for a few of my best collaborators, and work began there three months later on the north side of Issy-les-Moulineaux.[9] André Lefebvre,[10] who would one day play a leading technical role at Citroën, was my director. Another of my spiritual sons, Fernand Viallet,[11] was at my side. This new enterprise was pleasingly uncomplicated, and our research programme extended from engines to heavy aircraft.

The *Laboratoire* had but one fault: it was directly in the line of fire of 'Bertha', the German artillery's long-distance canon.[12] But the shells of this extraordinary ballistic device had no great effect.

In 1914, we foresaw nothing of the Russian Revolution that was to occur towards the end of the war. We were familiar with the experience of the Communards of 1871, and I well knew from personal testimonies that it had not been a great success… I had of course read Karl Marx, but his writings had never struck me as the new Gospel. Nevertheless, according to my fellow Parisian industrialists, I was a dangerous revolutionary. I belonged to no union or trade association and operated on the margins of accepted convention.

---

9) On the rue Guynemer between the Voisin and SEV factories and excluded from the sale to Lefebvre, this was the famous *Laboratoire* after which the C6 and other competition Voisin cars became known.

10) One of the first graduates of what was to become the École Nationale Supérieure de l'Aéronautique et de Construction Mécanique (Sup'Aéro), **André Lefebvre** joined Voisin at the age of 22 in March 1916 and had worked alongside GV on the design and development of Voisin bombers.

11) Viallet remained with GV until 1958.

12) A common misconception at the time. *Big Bertha* (after Frau Krupp) never shelled Paris; the ordnance in question arrived via the *Wilhelmgeschutze*, whose 78-mile range was designed to reach London from the French coast.

In my own company, I had applied that which seems to me indispensable for a group of men pursuing a common goal: 30 years before the official creation of 'worker representatives', I had introduced a system of elected delegates from both the office staff and the factory floor. We had effective health insurance arrangements in place, and our medical service was overseen with exceptional competence by the medical director of *La Pitié*, Doctor Thiroloix.[13]

One of my main concerns resulted from the irksome dichotomy between cerebral work and manual labour. I know full well how to use my hands, and I take great pride in this ability because I appreciate what the rigorous disciplines of manual work can bring to an able professional. There were few 'intellectuals' in my firm, but this minority would stick together to form what I regarded as a potentially dangerous element in an enterprise based on unshared technical values.

The day after I sold the company, a handful of agitators besieged my successor. This man had absolutely no idea of what an original creation involves - that is, the process of imagining that which does not yet exist, then designing and building it. He leant a receptive ear to the insinuations of a few ignoramuses and gave these unfortunates free rein to display their talents. This manifested itself in an 'entirely new' aeroplane which was apparently going to revolutionise aviation.[14] The result of this stupidity was no better than it deserved to be. The super-plane struggled to leave the ground. This pile of scrap was endlessly modified, and the adventure ended in technical and financial disaster.

13) Widely published and justly famed, **Jules-Alexandre Thiroloix** ran Paris' old-established *Hôpital la Pitié-Salpétrière*, once the largest hospital in the world. Voisin had also been one of th first employers to set up a staff pension scheme.

14) This must refer to the Voisin Type XII night bomber of 1918. Though more conventional than its predecessors, with a 30m wingspan and four 220hp Hispano engines, its demise was more due to its lateness than any underperformance.

I then received in my *laboratoire* an unofficial visit from two representatives. These men were loyal, perfectly sensible old friends. Our brief conversation can be summarised as follows:

"You left us, and the effects of your decision are plain to see. If we don't succeed in persuading you back to the place that's rightfully yours, all our efforts, enthusiasm and commitment will not be enough to save the company."

A similar delegation from our subcontractors confirmed the situation. It was all but impossible for me to act. But a few days later, my successor came to see me on some pretext or other. His visit was not disinterested. In a few words, he explained that, if I had not already disposed of the funds I had acquired from the sale, it would be profitable for me to invest such moneys as I had available in the Voisin company. A prodigious sum - and to complete the package, I would have the highly remunerated position of consultant chief engineer.[15]

The balance in my current account at the time was very substantial indeed. Half an hour after this interview, my successor strode quickly across the old training ground. He had in his wallet a cheque for six million 1917 francs.[16]

I did of course have allies in the factory. The day after this transaction, I knew that the money had been duly incorporated into the company's capital.

Later, my finance director was wrestling with some intractable problems in our branches in the provinces, one of which faced very severe difficulties within a month of my payment to the Voisin company.

15) The contract also entitled GV to royalties and a percentage of profits.

16) This transaction took place early in the Spring of 1918.

By some dazzling sleight of hand, the bulk of my funds had been unceremoniously transferred from the Issy-les-Moulineaux account to the coffers of the struggling subsidiary. As is so often the case, a little later the business in question paid its shareholders a dividend, which in turn led to promotions and pay rises, thanks to which, et cetera…

Forewarned on the very day of this fraudulent transfer, I waited patiently for the moment when I would present a letter to the presiding magistrate informing him of my situation. A confrontation then precipitated events; the magistrate appointed an expert accountant, and after a few weeks of wrangling, I once again resumed the heavy yoke of running my company. This process had cost me relatively dear, but it had the advantage of establishing the monetary value of my enterprise.

In summary, this sale would have made me a millionaire, and as everyone knows, a millionaire whose millions are in the form of land, factories, raw materials and a business can afford to look to the future with some optimism.

The armistice was signed a little later. On the morning of November the 12th 1918, I had the pleasure of banning from the Voisin factory all these gentlemen from the inspection department. Without losing a moment, I called a halt to all production and with great relief sold off everything remotely connected with aeroplanes.

I was 38 years old, in excellent health and very proud. I enjoyed the confidence of the men who surrounded me, and I knew how to hold a pencil. It wasn't a question of being 'optimists'. We were quite simply certain of succeeding in our endeavours.

—m—

Gabriel Voisin aboard *La Foudre* in July 1912, standing by the tail-mounted Gnome radial of the amphibious Voisin *canard*

Chapter 1

During my absence from the Voisin company, the situation had become more complicated, technically speaking. From 1909 to 1914, I had supplied the French and Russian navies with seaplanes[1] which had been enthusiastically received, and for which the Société Voisin (for my short-lived successor had transformed my business into a limited company[2]) had taken some orders.

The hulls and floats of this type of craft needed testing. As I knew from tiresome experience, such trials couldn't be conducted on the Seine. My machines had previously taken off from the river between the Pont de Peupliers and the Auteuil viaduct, then from the *trou salé* at Buc, and finally, the étang de Saclay, none of which had proved suitable for the purpose of researching the tractive effort required for flight.[3]

Our deliveries to the French Navy took place in Saint-Raphaël on the Mediterranean, where, for the first time in the world, a seaplane was mounted on a warship: *La Foudre.*[4] This was before the centre of Fréjus even existed. I therefore needed a relatively sheltered stretch of water nearby, and bought some land at Canoubiers bay in Saint-Tropez and

---

1) GV created the world's first operational seaplane by fitting plywood floats to his *canard* pusher biplane, which was first flown from the Seine at Billancourt in 1911. The subsequent model, with a fixed stabiliser and separate elevators, was delivered to the French navy early in 1912 as one of its first three aeroplanes. Tested at Fréjus in June, it was destroyed in August and replaced by a more conventional Voisin 13.5 metre seaplane, along with machines from other manufacturers.

2) The Société Anonyme Charles Lefebvre Aéroplanes G. Voisin.

3) GV had nearly drowned in this stretch of river at the controls of the glider he constructed in 1905 to Louis Blériot's design, while being towed by powerboat on the same day as his successful flight in the boxkite he built for Ernest Archdeacon.

4) *La Foudre* was converted into a seaplane carrier in 1912. The first naval trials of the Voisin *hydro canard* took place in April/May.

Gabriel Voisin (*right*) stands in front of the amphibious version of the Voisin 13.5m biplane at Fréjus in 1913.

acquired a boat in Cannes. Once it was moored in the small, rather exposed dock at Canoubiers, I made preparations to begin the test programme. An old undersea cable factory with its own quay would have fitted the bill, but no deal could be struck. Then a bureaucrat from some naval department or other had an attack of 'espionitis'. I was duly summoned, remorselessly interrogated and obliged to defend my activities. Although the official accusation of espionage was dropped, the slur remained.

Saint-Tropez in 1917 was not as it is in 1961. The inhabitants had little contact with the rest of France, and I was subjected to all kinds of idiocy. Anonymous letters eventually reached Toulon, where I was summoned three times to appear before a motley tribunal of sorts, to whom I had to explain myself, divulge trade secrets and account for allegedly suspicious goings-on. I was accused of 'making fires', that is to say signalling to a (then nonexistent) enemy. A rumour then started that my vessel was being used to supply German submarines.

I promptly ordered the Voisin company to cancel the seaplane contracts, sold the shed and the land, and set sail for Cannes harbour. My wife had acquired a very fine house, *Capo di Monte*,[5] and this beautiful property became our enchanted hideaway.

This episode was only an interlude. I soon found myself alone in Paris once again, where the most dangerous temptations awaited.

A real industrialist controls his empire from an office whose discreet luxury nevertheless suggests wealth. Real industrialists are surrounded by telephones, and however important the meeting that has been convened, it's impossible to have any worthwhile conversation with them - the telephone rings so often that it's best to give up trying altogether.

---

5) Bought with the proceeds of the sale of the company to Lefebvre, this villa complex was at 77, Avenue du roi Albert I[er], Cannes. GV sold the property to the celebrity mystic Meher Baba in 1937; it no longer exists.

The Captain's table in the First Class dining room of the *Ile de France* in 1928, en route from Le Havre to New York with the newly wed Janine Voisin. The smiling bride sits to her father's right, partially obscuring her new husband, Gifford Pinchot II. Between them sits the former air secretary and future prime minister of France, Pierre Flandin. The quantum physicist and Nobel laureate James Franck is at the head of the table next to Mme Voisin, with the wife of the poet diplomat Paul Claudel to the Captain's left. The sumptuous décor of the room itself - the largest afloat at the time – was designed by GV's architectural collaborator Pierre Patou.

That I've never been taken seriously is therefore perfectly understandable; indeed, it's only by happenstance that I succeeded in getting an office at all. The poky little cubbyhole in which I used to draw my designs had no telephone, and the drawing board that occupied most of the space was unprepossessing, to say the least. Deploring this Bohemianism, I resolved every week without fail to make more conventional arrangements. But in 1927, I completely abandoned my plans for a proper office. My daughter Janine[6] married Gifford Pinchot II, a young American engineer and son of the Governor of Pennsylvania. I accompanied her to the United States, along with my wife.[7]

It proved easy to meet Henry Ford, who received me immediately - and I was amazed to discover that this extraordinary man had no telephone on his desk, either. Whenever he wanted to give me some information or other, he did so not by pressing intercom buttons, but by turning round in his chair and tapping his pencil on the glazed partition. A secretary then opened the door, and a typewritten note with the requested information would arrive minutes later. In other words, I had unknowingly been copying the world's greatest industrialist...

On November 12th 1918, after having rid my life of all the highs and lows that aviation had brought me, I promptly set about executing the project I had been nursing for the past year: following the example of André Citroën, I wanted to convert my factory from making weapons of war to manufacturing automobiles.

6) At the time, GV's only daughter was hailed in the popular press as the most beautiful woman in France. The previous year, at the age of 17, she had refused a proposal of marriage from Alberto Santos-Dumont. Janine married Pinchot in Boulogne-sur-Seine in November 1928, and three weeks later GV and his wife accompanied the newlyweds to their new Manhattan home. GV attended the International Civil Aeronautics Conference in Washington before flying (courtesy of one of Henry Ford's fleet) to the International Aeronautical Exposition in Chicago. They sailed back home for Christmas..

7) **Adrienne-Dolores Bernet** (known as Lola), whom GV met at the world's first air meet at Reims in August 1909, and married later that year. In his 1936 preface to *L'Auto et l'Amérique* (Louis Bonneville, Dunod), GV writes that this visit to Ford took place in 1930 rather than December 1928, so it may have been a different occasion.

Charles (*left*) and Gabriel (*below*) Voisin in the two versions of the car they confected from a job lot of Audibert & Lavirotte parts in 1899. Nonconformist from the start, the teenage GV mounted its Aster engine transversely in an underslung frame, with four seats in *dos-à-dos* configuration above the back axle.

Bottom left: GV tows the tail of Delagrange's 10-metre Voisin cellular biplane by steamer to the Bagatelle polo ground in 1907.

In *Mes dix mille cerfs volants*, I recounted the story of two crude but quite functional motorcars my brother Charles[8] and I had designed and built near Lyon around 1900.

Since then, I had done nothing more than modify some of the many second-hand motorcars that passed through my hands. In 1904, I had acquired a Stanley steamer,[9] then one of our clients gave me a steam powered Serpollet;[10] after that, I also had Weyer (*sic*) et Richemond steamer.[11]

I wasn't alone in my interest in this type of car. At around the same time, my old friend Ettore Bugatti[12] also drove Stanleys, and later, a White whose perfection astounded us.

These cars were marvels of elaborate ingenuity. They ran in incomparable silence, and with flexibility unheard of in the internal combustion engines of the time. But they were of course only suitable for the mechanically competent who were prepared to travel with a voluminous toolkit.

---

8) Two years GV's junior, **Charles Voisin** in 1907 became the third man in Europe (after Clément Ader and Santos-Dumont) to fly a powered heavier-than-air machine. After an acrimonious disagreement between the two brothers in 1911, he died the following year in a road accident at the wheel of his Hispano at Corcelles, in the Beaujolais.

9) Acquired at a bankruptcy sale, the Stanley was updated by GV with Serpollet components and used to tow the first Voisin biplanes from the Billancourt factory to the few locations from which they were permitted to carry out trials.

10) The client in question was almost certainly **Ernest Archdeacon**, who was an important catalyst in GV's early career, as well as in the development of French aviation as a whole. In 1890, Archdeacon accompanied Léon Serpollet in a Peugeot-Serpollet steam tricycle from Paris to Lyon - the first ever long journey in arguably the first ever proper automobile   and contested the great road races of the nineties. GV's adroitness in fixing the iced-up carburettor on his Renault convinced the wealthy Franco-Scottish lawyer to employ him for his continuing aeronautical experiments.

11) Agricultural machinery manufacturers Weyher & Richemond ventured into automobile production in 1905.

12) According to the foreword GV penned for L'Ébé's *The Bugatti Story,* he had been friends with Ettore since 1908. Bugatti, like Voisin, was still designing steam engines during the 1940s.

Above: Lorraine-Dietrichs had finished 4th and 6th in the second Targa Florio in 1907, driven by Arthur Duray and Fernand Gabriel. GV's 8.5 litre car (seen here with the owner at the wheel, towing a Voisin *canard*) was probably obtained from either Duray or Henri Rougier, both of whom bought 10m Voisin biplanes and later became works drivers. Since Rougier had a business selling second-hand Isottas and Lorraines at the time, he seems the most likely source.

Top left: Les Frères Voisin (the world's first aeroplane manufacturing company) moved from its original premises in rue de la Ferme to this former sawmill on the West bank of the Seine at the Quai du Point du Jour in March 1908.

My first multi-cylinder internal combustion car was a Rochet-Schneider, which was replaced in 1909 by a so-called racer - a Lorraine Dietrich *Targa Florio*. It was on this car, with its four monstrous cylinders, that I first became acquainted with the dangers of speed. The Lorraine Dietrich had absolutely infernal steering. I don't think I've ever encountered anything as dangerously unpredictable as this stubbornly wilful mechanism: vague, sloppy, too low-geared, and prone to dreadful kickback and shimmy. I had nevertheless dismantled the monster's axle, realigned it and inclined it both forward and backward. Nothing came of my attempts, until the day when the steering accidentally seized. I was on the road to Mantes, by no means a motorway, when I came upon a freshly cobbled stretch. As the section under repair was quite long, I drove through it as fast as possible. Suddenly, the steering hardened slightly, and the finger-breaking shimmy disappeared as if by magic.

The Voisin factory was then at the Quai du Point du Jour in Billancourt. I returned to base, still astonished by the disappearance of these formidable oscillations, and went straight to the assembly shop to discover the reason for the transformation.

In his captivating book on Etruscanology, Edmond Bloch[13] complains bitterly about the procedures adopted for archaeological digs before 1900, and calls for the immediate application of statigraphic methods for accurately determining the various layers of substrate. I had known since our very first kites and mechanical constructions the care that has to be taken when drawing conclusions from an apparently inexplicable incident, and I systematically applied statigraphic methods. I duly submitted my Lorraine-Dietrich first to the ordinary question, then to the extraordinary one.

---

13) Professor Raymond Bloch, whose *Les Étrusques* was published in 1960; by 'statigraphic', GV meant stratigraphic in the sense of a methodical examination of the available evidence.

The front left stub axle bearing had indeed seized because of the introduction of a foreign body. There had been a lot of play in the steering bearings, and a shard of flint had embedded itself in the bronze bush concerned.

I effected a repair and took the car for a short test run. The shimmy was worse than ever. When I wedged a thick washer between the two surfaces, the steering became stiffer but the shimmy once again disappeared. I then understood that the weakness of many steering systems (even now, in 1961) was the pendulum effect induced by suspension movement, and immediately fitted a crude shock absorber consisting of a friction damper locked solidly to the front axle which rubbed against the track rod between the front wheels, thereby partially attenuating the oscillations. The effect was magical.

After the frightful *Targa Florio*, I owned a Belgian Métallurgique for a time. An agreeable enough mode of transport, but I had to exchange it against a commandeered Mercedes. This was followed by a 16CV Panhard with a Knight sleeve-valve motor, quite unlike the excellent Panhards of 1961. The steering was an undistinguished bit of ironmongery, and the height of the chassis and transmission predicated an entirely unacceptable centre of gravity. Enough said.

In 1917 I attempted to collate the results of all my observations since 1900, and soon realised with some surprise and anxiety how ill-equipped I was for the entirely new profession on which I was about to embark. I had none of my own data to draw upon, and could never in a few weeks hope to bridge the enormous gap between my merely superficial knowledge of automobile manufacture and the real thing.

In the manner still honoured by manufacturers of so-called modern cars, I could have acquired two or three of what were considered the best chassis, taken them apart and copied them.

Admittedly, I refrained from so doing not because of any scruples, but because of the certainty of thereby perpetuating errors that would compromise the end result.

My sales and marketing resources were nonexistent. The only way I could hope to succeed, which remains the only infallible one, was to offer the buyer the best possible product, with a clearly defined proposition.

If in any doubt as to the truth of this axiom, consider a recent example. The Citroën 2CV is by no means perfect - but ever since it appeared, and despite endless denigration, it has been consistently successful without the benefit of any advertising. The reason is simple: in a completely new way, it satisfies the consumer's requirements.

My attempt of 1917, although purely schematic, made me cautious. I wanted another string to my bow, and with the help of my two friends Noël[14] and Patou,[15] both accredited architects, I sketched out a prototype for super-economical housing.

Constructed entirely in steel, the accommodation consisted of prefabricated 12 x 2.5 metre 'slices'. The site could be prepared and the modules delivered and welded together in three days.

---

14) Nicknamed 'le pigeon', **André-Noël Noël Telmont** first met GV while both were studying architecture at the *atelier préparatoire* of Godefroy & Freynet in 1900, and the two became lifelong friends – indeed, he lived in GV's boulevard Exelmans house for years. He was trained in the school of Jean-Louis Pascal, whose mantra was, tellingly, "logic, not intuition. Simplify: only rational plans and decorous elevations." During the Great War, GV arranged for Noël Noël to enter a Voisin squadron; by 1918 he was chief instructor at the Avord flying school, having trained 1500 pilots. On joining the company after hostilities, he worked closely with GV on designing the coachwork of virtually every model; the distinctive Voisin aesthetic is therefore attributable to Noël as much as it is to GV.

15) Another almost exact contemporary of GV's, **Pierre Patout** in 1910 co-founded one of the first group practices in Paris, Levard, Noël and Ardelet. Two years after GV had commissioned him to build his own house at 13, allée des Pins, Billancourt, Patou became famous for the Cubist-influenced neoclassical buildings he created for the influential 1925 *Exposition des Arts Décoratifs et Industriels Modernes*, including the Porte de la Concorde and Ruhlmann's *Hôtel d'un Collectionneur*, which typified the style he later adopted for the interiors of the ocean liners *Normandie, Ile-de-France* and *Atlantique*.

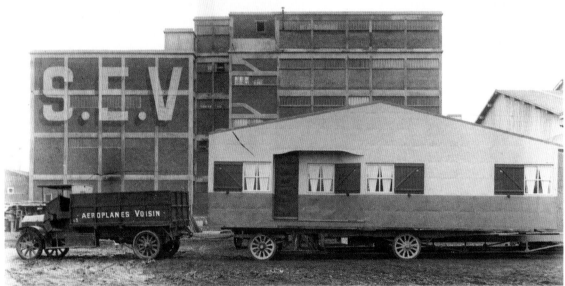

The *Maisons Voisin* (seen above on the former drill ground near the factory complex) were constructed around a steel framework clad in panels of a galvanised steel outer skin with a granular finish, and an aluminium inner skin with a layer of insulation between the two (patent 500.488), and came complete with a Voisin serial number on an identity plate above the chimney breast. In an article entitled *Les Voisin Maison* in the seminal modern movement publication *L'Esprit Nouveau 2* (1920), Le Corbusier and Amédée Ozenfant lavished great praise on the concept of houses "assembled like Ford automobiles," transported by road and erected on site within three days.

My friend Piat[16] organised the construction of one example, and by January 1919, our new homes were ready for delivery.

The project began well, then the orders dried up. Our homes didn't fully satisfy certain requirements; we were criticised, especially in the North, for internal condensation on the walls. We hadn't allowed for the fact that some of our customers' families would indulge in such vast amounts of laundering that our hermetically sealed homes soon filled with the steam from their washing machines...

Eventually the developers united in their opposition to what they saw as a threat, and demand proved insufficient. Although our *Maisons* technical service was perfectly organised by the end of 1918, I had to suspend manufacture, retaining the best technical ideas for re-use in the coachwork of our cars.

In February 1919, I wanted to collate a number of plans for these buildings as I lacked a complete set. Opening the door of my little office I saw the office boy shuffling along the corridor, and sent him to the far side of the factory to fetch the drawing I needed.

After a 20-minute wait, my door was opened by a very young woman bringing me drawings of the centre section of our buildings. She was dressed in a white short-sleeved blouse, her full figure encircled by a blue leather belt. My eyes lingered for an instant on a movingly beautiful neck before finally seeing her face. Beneath strawberry blond hair, she had perfect oval features. Her lips were half-open in a shy smile, and her eyes, when she spoke, were emeralds flecked with gold.

---

16) **Piat** had worked with Bénégent, one of the pioneers of oxyacetylene welding in France (who built the Sirius monoplane of welded steel tubing in mid-1910) and became foreman of the Voisin factory in 1913 to oversee production of the 13.5m all-steel Voisin light bomber that was the foundation of GV's wartime fortune.

She disappeared. I immediately sought out Albert Decarme, the former boss of the Point du Jour whom we affectionately nicknamed *Le Pateau*.[17]

"Albert, have you seen that young blonde who..."

"She's called Marianne. But watch out - her father or her brother come to fetch her every lunchtime and evening. She's drawing up your cabins..."

To this information, he added a remark he often used about women: "Tasty chick, that."

Next day, the 'tasty chick' was leaning over my drawing board, explaining assembly details in a tremulous voice. As I expressed surprise at the acuity of her remarks, she told me that she was preparing for a degree in architecture at the *Beaux Arts*. One of my architect friends had introduced her to the company, where she had been working for some weeks.

Marianne came every day to tell me what had been decided about assembly procedures. I made no progress whatsoever in reaching her inner self, but the gods were keeping watch. One April day, we were both poring over a drawing when she began sketching out in pencil a fixing she proposed. By placing my hand on hers, I stopped her in mid-flow. Marianne was silent for a minute. Then she laid her head on my hand.

This I had not expected. My draughtswoman was a good girl, and her gesture made me lose my bearings. Putting my hands on her shoulders, I drew her towards the high stool on which I sat. Her cool arms knotted around my neck, and finally her emerald eyes met mine.

---

17) Also nicknamed *le homard* (both this and *poteau* being Parisian slang derivatives of *homme* and *pote* respectively), the former pimp and petty criminal Decarme had saved GV's life in 1905 by fishing him out of the Seine as he struggled to free himself from the tangle of piano wires of the ditched Voisin Blériot glider. Decarme's stint at *Voisin Frères* was interrupted by a two-year prison stretch for GBH, but he later personally bailed out the ailing company with 100,000 francs of his own money as it teetered on the edge of bankruptcy (for neither the first nor the last time) in 1914.

"I'm going," she said, and with that she left my tiny office. Not a word had been exchanged between us. For a month, I had been rehearsing who knows what protestations, because although I had revealed to her none of the feelings which so agitated me, Marianne occupied all my thoughts. She returned the next day, and I finally found out why she had rested her head on my hand.

"I was very young when I first saw you at Issy, where I live with my parents and my brother, and I can't tell you how long I have loved you without ever giving you the slightest hint of my feelings. Now you know…"

Three months passed with brief meetings in my little office, or around the factory. Marianne, as Albert had said, was under strict surveillance. A virginal 20 year-old, her parents had her destined for an uncomplicated marriage.

In December 1918[18] I saw her one morning, absolutely transformed.

"I'm alone at home for two days," she declared.

"Marianne, let's dine together tonight…"

She accepted. I met her in the place de la Concorde and took her to *Aux Fleurs*, a restaurant in the rue Lauriston with a large ground floor dining area and private rooms on the floor above. These had none of the dubious propriety of the private rooms in some other establishments; with one side open to the chandeliers illuminating the main space, they had no connotations of clandestine trysts. And besides, *Aux Fleurs* boasted an excellent band.

Marianne was innocent of everything that could be called Parisian life. I sat close to her,

18) More probably in the summer of 1919.

but our dinner together was less than lively. My guest adopted a reserve that impressed me. Over dessert, she reached out her hand, which I clasped to my heart. I listened.

"You know how much I love you," she said, "and you know I am yours. I shall probably become your mistress. You are married; I am constantly being watched over. My life will become the furtive existence that many women have to suffer. I'll wait for opportunities for us to meet, just as I have waited three months for this moment we are living tonight. I shall never be a happy..."

The orchestra was playing Ravel's *Alborado Gracioso*. I took Marianne in my arms, guided her to the divan and knelt close. Once again, I was experiencing the sparkling miracle of love. Just then, Marianne shook with an unstoppable sob, a sob which was to prove our salvation. I suggested a compromise:

"Let's wait - I love you, and have but one desire: to see you happy. Neither of us knows what the future holds..."

I accompanied my beloved home. We met every day. Marianne had happened too late, but she was what I had been waiting for. The restaurant adventure was repeated twice in the ensuing six months. Still we waited.

One day in 1919, Marianne was absent from work - suffering from 'flu, as it turned out. A little later, that same influenza which took my dearest friend, Léon Morane,[19] also robbed me of this beauty whose presence in my life had so enchanted me.

---

19) The pioneer aviator **Léon Morane** fell victim to the Spanish flu epidemic in October of the previous year. The first to fly at over 100kph (in a Blériot in 1910), he founded Aéroplanes Morane-Saulnier with his brother Robert and Raymond Saulnier in 1911. There is no evidence that, as some say, it was Morane who originally financed the development of the prototype of what became the Voisin M1.

Grief stricken, I cursed our circumspection. I didn't yet know that Marianne was to be the last great love of my life. I was to meet other women and enjoy other tender moments, but I had exhausted the unforgettable leaps of great passion...

From 1918, my time was divided between *Capo di Monte*, Cannes and Issy-les-Moulineaux. My wife and daughter came to Paris every autumn. Though our house on the boulevard d'Auteuil in Boulogne was perfectly agreeable, it lacked charm to my eyes whenever I was there alone. I therefore bought a plot surrounded by gardens at 72 Boulevard Exelmans, where I had a hideaway built that the rumour mill immediately christened 'the stud farm'.

My hideaway was a fantasy. I furnished it reasonably well,[20] and laid it out for entertaining friends. Beside a big hallway which could be transformed into a small theatre, there was a bedroom and a blue bathroom that effectively consisted of an enormous swimming pool. The rest of the house was in keeping, but for the gossipmongers, the whole building along with its theatre and pool reeked of dissolution and debauchery. Nothing remotely immodest ever happened there, however. The eventual fate of this home I shall recount later.

In Cannes, where I stayed while chassis testing, life went on agreeably. My wife patiently awaited my visits; by and large, we were happy together. My daughter was growing up, and my gorgeous sisters-in-law filled *Capo di Monte*. I flirted with them far too much; as they were all three rather lonely, I would brush past these all too seductive sisters in a flower-bedecked home in a truly splendid location - very agreeable moments. My sisters-in-law are now with the Lord, having brought to my life a fragrant tenderness that I shall never forget...

---

20) An understatement. The house was largely furnished and decorated by Jacques-Emile Ruhlmann (1879-1933), a prominent exhibitor at the *Exposition Internationale des Arts Décoratifs* a few years later, and one of a small coterie of fashionable designers producing extravagantly luxurious interiors in the *moderne* style for the social élite.

In 1908, at the time when Henry Farman clinched the official record for the first flight around a closed kilometre circuit in one of my machines, my brother Charles suggested that we celebrate with a dinner at Maxim's in the rue Royale. That day, I immediately became friends with Gustave Cornuché and his excellent house, which later became a favourite venue for agreeable soirées with friends.

From 1913, I lunched there practically every day, meeting colleagues from the worlds of both aviation and the automobile. *Maxim's* in those days was not the caravanserai it is now; despite the ever-open door, it was a closed circle for the few.

Not that there was any question of entrance committees or proposing members, of course. But undesirables only ever came once. Passing judgement in a matter of minutes, Gustave Cornuché would make them feel unwelcome. They were served between gritted teeth, and handed bills so cripplingly exorbitant that they would mark the place with a black cross and never return.

Among the regulars in 1917 was a young man whose repartee was always spirited. Artaud[21] by name, he worked in the technical department at Panhard. I happened one day in 1918 to talk about cars with him, mentioning in confidence my plans for converting my factories to automobile production. This made him smile.

"I hope," he said, "you have plenty of time and money, because embarking on such a difficult new enterprise can be costly..."

I asked him what he meant. "It's relatively easy," he explained, "for a competent engineer

---

21) Starting out as a riding mechanic to Georges Teste in 1905, **Ernest Artault** became a well connected wheeler-dealer in Parisian automotive circles. Before 1914, had been a business partner, test driver, consultant and agent for Panhard, reporting directly to Arthur Krebs and his board; he may also have been an agent for Knight & Kilbourne.

to design and construct a power unit. But when you get to the bench testing stage, what comparators do you have to guide you? It won't have escaped your notice that, rightly or wrongly, manufacturers operate in the strictest secrecy. You'll therefore be in trouble right from the start, simply because you have no previous experience to draw upon."

"I have seen a few engines in my time," I replied.[22]

"I'm sure you have. But do you know all the tolerances, the clearances, everything that makes the difference between a good machine and a bad one? It takes a lot of experience to produce a car that meets the requirements of an exacting clientèle, whose high expectations you're all too familiar with. You don't know the secret little technical trick that allows some usually overlooked component to be efficiently lubricated, and insignificant as it may be in itself, such a minor detail can spell serious problems for a new marque under the super-critical scrutiny of its competitors.

"I did tackle the odd problem or two in aviation, you know!"

"Of course - but very different ones. If your conversion plans grind to a halt, by all means carry out a design study - but I think that before long I'll be in a position to offer you a suitable solution."

I pressed on with my design. The man was right. The major components were easy, but I suddenly realised that the tremendous importance of the nitty gritty, the little grommets and gauges, the thousands of fixings, all the hardware that has to be made to a price. A few weeks later in March 1918, Artaud came to see me at Issy-les-Moulineaux.

---

22) Quite apart from a decade's experience with the aero engines of other manufacturers, GV had In fact already designed and built his own power unit eight years previously - a 5.9 litre four-cylinder unit delivering 40hp at 1100rpm, which powered the firm's experimental tractor biplane.. It was not successful.

With the aid of fellow Panhard engineer Louis Dufresne, a graduate of the *École Centrale*, he proposed a remodelled and lightened version of the 16CV Panhard. A prototype had been built, but nothing had ensued. Artaud and Dufresne then acquired the prototype and the designs, and they both offered the car to André Citroën, who was also planning to convert his munitions factory.[23]

Citroën didn't enter into things lightly. He had the prototype tested and ordered three Artaud-Dufresne cars to be built in his workshops. The car was pleasing, but the man from Quai de Javel felt that it was too luxurious for his purposes and offered me the designs and the four prototypes as a job lot. I accepted, and lost no time in setting to work.

On June 1st 1918 at Issy-les-Moulineaux, we started designing the tooling and hastily began constructing a one-off chassis with certain detail modifications.[24]

---

23) Dufresne began working on the design in 1915; the first prototype was shown to Citroën the following year, almost certainly for consideration as a post-war Mors (a marque whose fortunes he had succeeded in reviving with a new range boasting Knight sleeve valve engines before the war).

24) The chronology of the original 'ADC' (Artault, Dufresne, Cabaillot) prototypes is confused. The first chassis was offered for homologation at the *Service des Mines* in January 1918 - two months before GV says Artault presented his designs. However, there are Voisin factory drawings of the chassis dated even earlier, in the summer of 1917, so it seems probable that the question of finding a car to manufacture arose soon after GV learned in February that the military would no longer be ordering Voisin bombers. With a 2,000-strong workforce to occupy, it was a matter of diversify or die. This timing accords with Wolgensinger´s biography of Citroën, which suggests that he offered GV the design in mid-1917. As these negotiations predate the sale of the company to Charles Lefebvre, the project must have been conducted in some secrecy.

Chapter 11

When my hideaway in boulevard Exelmans was ready, I organised a housewarming party.

Visiting Paul Iribe[1] and other friends, I had met a number of women remarkable for their beauty, elegance and spirit. I shan't name them - you find traces of their influence in any account of Parisian life of the 1920s. These ladies accepted my invitation, and it goes without saying that all my friends from the world of aviation and society in general attended the ceremony. I say 'ceremony' because at first the dinner for some reason took on a ceremonial air. Over dessert, however, the pianist Victor Gilles[2] (*sic*) agreed to entertain us, and his considerable talent succeeded in breaking the ice.

Beside the famous blue mosaic pool, I had installed a vast wardrobe containing every imaginable type of fancy dress. Feather boas lay next to chasubles, and there was a whole array of wigs and false beards. As soon as I revealed these to our guests, fantasy took over.

By suppertime, smoking jackets and evening gowns had disappeared without trace around the big table. My high-spirited guests having pillaged the fancy dress cupboard, I saw only ladies bedecked with all their finery and long-haired swains, real or assumed.

---

1) Graphic artist, furniture designer, decorator, caricaturist and journalist, **Paul Iribe** (1883-1935) began his career as an artist for the satirical weekly *L'Assiette au Beurre*, and later became involved with high fashion, notably for the couturier Paul Poiret (a Voisin owner often mistakenly credited for designing the upholstery fabrics for the factory) and Jeanne Lanvin (another celebrity Voisin owner). He later married Coco Chanel.

2) A pupil and leading interpreter of Chopin and confidant of Empress Eugénie and Queen Victoria, **Victor Gille** was an outrageously eccentric pianist who affected 18th century manners and dress, with full white make-up and rouge, wearing lace ruffles but laceless shoes, believing it unhygienic to touch footwear.

Eventually, a show of sorts was organised - a succession of chaotic vignettes, *tableaux vivants* that were anything but, shrieks, dances and wild music. How the evening ended is unclear; I had the impression that, the table groaning with bottles, we were eventually overcome by sheer exhaustion. At dawn, on the sofas around my bedroom, on haphazardly thrown cushions, a highly eclectic cast of characters lay sleeping, with orientals nestling against courtiers, epées still at their sides.

Paris was soon buzzing with scandalous rumours and gossip about this housewarming, despite the fact that all the guests were well above the age of consent. The party reinforced the reputation foisted on me by the stupid and malicious. These scandalmongers only forgot one thing: all the employment I had created over 20 years, and the way in which I had acquired the means to receive my friends in the manner I saw fit.

At nearly three in the morning on the day of my 39th birthday on February 5th 1919, our first prototype chassis was ready. Though desperately cold, tired and miserable, the workshop team around me retained enough strength and naïve optimism to expect instant success.

I've never been able to find the right term to describe those who have accompanied me so bravely throughout my crazy life. 'Comrade' lacks nobility. I don't like 'collaborator'. 'Employee' is dishonourable, 'worker' impossible; 'proletarian' is out of the question. On the other side of the class divide, we have managed to find perfectly acceptable words: 'my associates', 'my principal shareholder'...

How to describe these men full of spirit, courage, rectitude and loyalty, virtually all of whom I have now lost?

In the world of work, there are two types of men - those who scrape a living in order to eat, and those who eat to be able to fulfil their potential. The former fell by the wayside within a few hours; the others were enlightened. Mme Descarmes (*sic*), Albert's wife, had one day said to her husband: "You and your boss, it's just not on. What has he done to make you love him more than me?"

The great team has now dispersed. Where are you, Emile, the tireless motivator, silent Teullières, Niedergang the born mechanic, Blanc the perfectionist, Chapy, the revolutionary we made out to be so dangerous but who was so dear to my heart? How strong we were, grouped around this intransigent machine of which we had such high hopes, newly fashioned with invincible courage by our own hands!

It was nevertheless a pressed steel chassis like so many others before and since. The fragile Knight sleeve-valve engine had exasperated us, with unending efforts to true up the cylinders, and its sleeves fusing together in the relentless heat of combustion.

This four-litre engine should have yielded 200 stampeding stallions, but only five days before, we had difficulty in extracting 80 ponies from it. We were discouraged by the four-speed and reverse gearbox, with its imbroglio of complex controls and its rumbling growl that was so hard to suppress amid the noise of so many bearings. Finally a driveshaft, that utterly cretinous idiocy, connected the front to the rear, transmitting and transforming the movement of the engine, parallel to the general axis of transverse movement. Forty years later, car designers still don't understand that the entire mechanism of their vehicles should be either at the front or the rear, and that the heavy, expensive, bulky assemblage of a conventional transmission is beyond redemption, with its bearings, balls, cages, thrust bearings, inadequate lubrication, and to cap it all, that ruinous meshing of angled gears fit only for machines of the devil.

2056   2057   1367   2085   2084   1572   1775   1569   1560   1559   1558

1550   1846   1454   1592   2020   1482   1479   1624   1566 dr

Finally, on the 5th of February 1919, our first Voisin chassis, the precursor of a glorious line, was ready for its first road test. Emile opened the doors of the annexe where we had been working. A bitter wind swept through the vast space, and shivering, I climbed aboard.

I sat on the pine box that took the place of its eventual coachwork and pushed the starter button. Obviously, the starter itself was a Bendix affair, with its myriad teeth whose racket remains shameful today. I heard the engine cough into life, engaged first gear and carefully let out the clutch. There was plenty of room in front of me, but piled up in apocalyptic disorder behind our masterpiece there lay a jumble of tools and toolboxes we had been using for endless adjustments during the night. I pressed the accelerator. My car took off a little brusquely, but it took off - backwards, knocking over the whole pile behind its fuel tank.

I declutched. My team grinned. Emile approached the monster to see which slot I'd engaged; I was in first, right enough. I tried again after we had all checked, and once more it started going backwards. I put it in reverse and took off - forwards.

Puzzled, my team gathered around and dismantled the mysterious beast that persisted in going backwards when instructed to go ahead and took the liberty of going forwards when reverse was required. The check was soon over. Stripping the back axle soon solved the mystery: the Gleason gear had been fitted back to front...

It was an understandable error. The final drive was symmetrical, and the crown wheel responsible could be fitted equally well on the right or left-hand side. My 'experts' wore long faces. They had worked day and night so that this test could take place on my 39th birthday, and this elementary mistake had dashed their hopes...

I therefore suggested a compromise. We never had any intention of going out for a spin at three in the morning on the day in question; we only wanted to find out whether our machine could move under its own power. So why not carry on with the first test in reverse?

Emile jumped onto the seat next to me, and I drove our creation out into the precincts of the annexe. This was an immense shed in which aeroplanes had been assembled only a few weeks earlier. It was situated north-east of Issy-les-Moulineaux' famous *champs de manoeuvres*, and I had built two kilometres of private road, five metres wide, to link it with the main factory workshops in boulevard Gambetta. The road was metalled, and at four o'clock on that February morning it was covered by a thin layer of ice that sparkled in the beam of my headlamps.

One of my improvements to the original prototype had been substantially to increase the size of the brake drums (which were of course only fitted at the rear, the very idea of front wheel brakes being regarded as highly contentious at the time[3]). I therefore drove at greatly reduced speed, since I only had one reverse gear with which to go forwards, and when I was half way along our private road, I applied the foot brake. The result was hardly what we had expected from our big drums - the chassis skidded immediately and gyrated nose to tail.

I tried again, with the same result. I then wanted to test our gearbox, but could only do so going backwards. I made the attempt; arriving at the halfway point, still icy, in second, and braking once more, I was amazed to see our chassis come to a halt without the slightest untoward movement. Emile suggested an explanation: like the transmission, the brake

3) Although the first FWB patent was in 1903, its use was pioneered by Perrot while working for Argyll in 1910. Having met with little interest in the UK, he took his ideas to the Continent. By 1914, Isotta Fraschini, Spyker, Sheffield-Simplex, Arrol-Johnston, Thames and some Rolland Pilain cars were thus equipped, along with Delage, Peugeot, Fiat and Piccard-Pictet racers. Delage road cars first had FWB in 1919, along with some Talbot-Darracq and Hispano-Suiza chassis.

shoes had been assembled back to front, so the linings were grabbing when going forwards, and biting progressively when braking in reverse.

Without discussing this setback, I drove our first production car back into the annexe, promising myself to clarify this question of brakes in peace and quiet. At 10 o'clock the next morning I took to our test track once again, and despite the better adhesion of a drier road surface, the results were more or less the same as I had observed in the frosty conditions of the night before.

I then had a box mounted on the back of our chassis, and progressively loaded it with weights equivalent to heavy bodywork on the assumption that this would increase rear wheel adhesion. This extra mass - some 300 kilos, by the end - only served to confirm my observations. The brakes, albeit only at the rear, were clearly very efficient, easily locking the wheels. I brought the chassis back to the workshop; the differential was taken apart and reassembled with the crown wheel the right way round. By the next morning, I was able to carry on with my tests.

The results being the same, the conclusion was obvious: a four-wheeled vehicle should be braked by the front wheels, not the rear.

How was it that so many of the experts in locomotion who had preceded me since Cugnot, back in the reign of Louis XV, had failed to grasp this basic truth and had not surmounted every obstacle in order to brake the front wheels? Simple. My forebears had probably never found themselves in the odd position of dealing with a wrongly assembled transmission - or if they had, they lacked the curiosity to learn from the experience by spending a few minutes analysing the result.

I then remembered having often seen peasant carts coming down the hill at Montanay near Neuville-sur-Saône, the brakes on the back wheels locked solid, sliding along on virtually stationary steel bands, criss-crossing the road alarmingly or progressing at a pronounced angle to the main shaft.

Thus, throughout the existence of rear wheel braked vehicles, no carriage maker, not one of all these men who had by their own inspired hands constructed everything from modest peasant carts to the grandest royal carriages, had had the idea of braking the front wheels and leaving the rears to carry out their proper guiding function, since a wheel that no longer turns at the speed with which it covers the ground ceases to have any useful directional effect.

The experience gave me an inkling of the vast accumulation of custom and practice that would need to be overturned, and I realised it would be necessary to fight the old battles of aeronautics anew - this time without the help of my brother Charles, who could grasp a phenomenon at the same instant that I observed it, and who had the knack of drawing immediate conclusions that were later proved correct.

However, I had to launch my first cars with rear wheel brakes only. Big problems are difficult to rectify in any series production. Once the inexorable machinery of a production line has started, the whole factory has to operate at a fixed rhythm - and even if a problem emerges requiring some major modification, the designer has to plan long in advance before it can appear on production models. By February 1919, the machine shop was in full swing, the cars were fitted out, components were at the final verification stage, and short of calling a complete halt to our activities, there was no way in which we could even think about modifying the braking system.

I waited - and I was right to do so, because a year later, front wheel braking systems made their appearance and I was soon able to choose between the systems on offer, ready for use. I chose Piganeau's excellent axle, a choice subsequently vindicated in practice. Piganeau was a mechanic, and his cable-operated mechanism met our needs admirably.

But if the advent of four-wheel brakes was inevitable, it occurred to none of my contemporaries to have the front predominating - that took another 30 years. Yet I was already carrying out my first tests of unequal front/rear brake balance in 1920. I decided on an 80% front bias, with only 20% on the rears. This arrangement gave us a considerable handling advantage under braking. The results were indisputable and easily demonstrated.

I still can't understand why this simple expedient of having levers of unequal length wasn't immediately spotted and copied by others. On later reflection, I realise that I had adopted this arrangement without discussing it with my entourage. In a word, the Voisin factory was itself unaware of the reason for our exceptional braking, and the first 18CV models left Issy-les-Moulineaux at a rate that seems paltry today, but was entirely satisfactory at the time.

It was when Lockheed appeared on the scene that our ploy was discovered. When I switched to hydraulic brakes,[4] I wanted larger cylinders at the front than the rear. A brief discussion and a simple test was all it took to convince Lockheed personnel, and front-wheel brake bias then became universal. However, it had taken some 25 years for automobile braking finally to become rational in its execution!

------

4) The C28 models were equipped with Lockheed hydraulic brakes from 1936, although hydraulic brakes (to a design by the former Voisin *canard* pilot Pierre Cayla, then a director of the company) had also featured on the second of the stillborn 12-cylinder C2 prototypes of 1922. Had it entered production, this ambitious creation would otherwise have been the first in the world with four-wheeled hydraulic brakes, just pipping the Model A Duesenberg by a few months.

A few refinements to the engine gave us a little more horsepower. The Voisin was a brilliant car; with proper coachwork it could easily maintain 120kph, a speed I think unequalled by other car of the same capacity (3,969cc) in France at the time. For the next 15 years, we made cars that held the crown of the road.

This superiority wasn't achieved by garish advertising.[5] It was often a question of arduous observations and apparently insignificant modifications, some prudent, some audacious - and our existence was always under threat from other manufacturers who had not bargained for new competitors forged by the war years, but who nevertheless began to realise that Citroën in the realm of popular cars, and ourselves in the luxury market, would make business more difficult for them. The nefarious cold war they waged against us made life very difficult. A conspiracy of silence surrounds the name of Voisin to this day, in aviation as well as in automobile circles, and any writer has to be particularly well informed about our work to cite our company alongside the sacred monsters.

These commercial shenanigans weren't the only cause of the problems to come. The depression of 1930 was to crush many companies, and my enterprise suffered cruelly, but there were other factors in the collapse of Voisin that I shall reveal later.

In 1920, one of the weaknesses of my business was my own inconstancy. In his *Description d'un voyage autour du monde*, de Bougainville[6] recounts how he found himself fêted with honours when he was received by the King at Versailles and complimented as only Louis XIV knew how. But, he continues, "my penchant for sex was to be my downfall."

5) True as this may be, Voisin advertised in a wide range of publications aimed at their target market, using a defiantly idiosyncratic creative approach in which GV was directly involved, as he was in writing the sales collateral for his cars.

6) The soldiering lawyer, mathematician and botanist Count **Louis de Bougainville** was the first Frenchman to circumnavigate the globe, and his 1772 account to which GV refers did much to popularise J-J Rousseau's ideas of the Noble Savage.

Bougainville tells us nothing more of this predilection, and we shall probably never know whether the great navigator was a glutton or a gourmet in these matters, but in short (and on a less grand scale), my situation was similar to his. Having spent several years battling the perils of the sea, he returned to France with such an accumulation of unspent ardour that it threatened his career.

Like the admiral, I had just emerged from the inhuman pressures of several years of worry. I had undergone four years of war under constraints as severe and dramatic as any front line commander, and when this appalling period eventually came to an end, I too at 39 years of age had a deep well of frustrated lust that prevailed over the exhausted pleasures of incessant hard, and often discouraging, work. Finally, for the first time in my life, I had the financial means which, as everyone knows, undoubtedly makes one attractive - 'cheque appeal'.

I had known many men thus obsessed. Generally, their smugly proclaimed prowess seemed to me ridiculous, an opinion reinforced by female confidences. The women I knew were attracted not by quantitative performance but a subtle sort of sympathetic magic that's hard to pin down, and whose pursuit, never having discovered 'the great secret', took up much of my time.

It was not just sex itself that appealed to me, as seems to have been the case with de Bougainville, but the intimacy of women. I appreciated their intelligence, their subtlety, their resistance, their surrender. I liked living their joys, sharing their difficult existence, and I knew well that in a few thousand years, masculine bluster, men's ineffable stupidity and pretensions would disappear from creation, because the spirit is always the victor in the battle of life.

LA VOITURE DE LUXE FRANÇAISE VOISIN

CONDUITE INTÉRIEURE quatre places

CONCESSIONNAIRES EXCLUSIFS

COMPAGNIE FRANÇAISE DES ÉTABLISSEMENTS

GASTON, WILLIAMS & WIGMORE

3, RUE TAITBOUT

PARIS (9e)

IMP. QUSSAC, PARIS.

54

My memories of 1919 and 1920 are confused. I must have been out on the town a lot with friends. I must also have entertained a great deal at boulevard Exelmans. In addition, I constantly had to oversee what went on at Issy-les-Moulineaux, conducting tests that took us from Paris to Mont Ventoux, with tiresome mechanical interventions en route, often at night far from anywhere, and in secret because a major repair in a country garage is a sure wrecker of reputations.

I also had to involve myself in matters of administration, schedules, production issues and finance, because very large sums were required to convert the factory. I lived in a constant state of extreme vigilance in order to maintain an effective defence against all the self-interested 'advisers' and assorted crooks whom my success had attracted.

We were able to offer our motorcar to quasi-international organisations, taking an order for 6,000 units from the Société Williams-Wigmore alone.[7] These orders were naturally accompanied by deposits, and millions danced before my eyes and in my ill-informed mind, unsuited as it was of the world of big business.

On the 30th December 1919, my friends were waiting for me at Maxim's. I had been told of a banquet being held to celebrate a choreographic triumph: Mademoiselle Damazzio had shone among the leading dancers of the company.

7) Though this figure is often dismissed as an exaggeration, Gaston Williams & Wigmore didn't think small. Founded in 1914 as procurement agents for the allied war effort, the American-owned trading company by then ran an empire stretching from Valparaiso to Vladivostok and a huge shipping fleet. André Lombard, the company's director in France, signed a similar contract with Salmson the following year to manufacture 3,000 GNs under licence. Gaston & Cie (as they became known in 1921) also held exclusive rights for Citroën in the UK until 1923. The company was typical of the international agents for manufactured goods that Keynes later held partially responsible for the post-war boom and crash, after facing insuperable trading difficulties when the currencies of commodity-producing countries collapsed in the early 1920s, when the deal GV mentions fell by the wayside. GWW appeared as exclusive concessionaires on the first press advertisement for Voisin, based on Jean Routier's 1919 drawing of a limousine with a distinctive bow-fronted windscreen.

I had been an habitué of l'Opéra since the heroic years of aviation, when the former secretary of the Commune in 1871 and minister of our republics[8] used to invite my wife to his private box. But my taste at the time being only for music, I did not patronise the *Foyer de Danse*.

I turned up at Maxim's at around 10 o'clock, accompanied by the two ladies responsible for my late arrival. They were both models, and hats in 1920 were as large as their dresses were short. We joined a group who had long since given up waiting for me, and whose elegance was measured neither by the length of their garments nor the size of their millinery. Their beautiful eyes widening at the apparel of my companions, the young women dining that night in rue Royale made laudable efforts not to burst out laughing. There were however many smiles, and one of the most delightful was right opposite the chair that the maitre d' had adroitly placed at my request in the middle of the group.

Gustave Cornuché was an incomparable master of ceremonies. With a wink, he would indicate the more excessive plumage, and the hats in question would be discreetly borne off to the cloakrooms. Hatless, my guests took their place at the centre of a group of friends.

The dinner went on and on. There were one or two polite compliments about the talent of the *grand sujet*, and dessert arrived in the form of a set piece which was apparently meant to be an allusion to Carpeaux' masterpiece, *La Danse*.[9] Eventually we were able to cut to the chase. I naturally invited the beautiful smiler in front of me, whose dazzling brilliance was all I had so far registered. A dancer from the Palais Garnier, she must have been about 20, about 5'3" and despite the beautiful legs I instantly noticed, she can have weighed no more

8) Gaston Thomson (who, although Minister for the Navy, was never in fact secretary to the Commune).

9) Jean-Baptiste Carpeaux had achieved notoriety 50 years earlier with this elaborate frieze of naked figures dancing with wild abandon above the Opéra de Paris. GV's brother-in-law Victor Margueritte had in 1913 written a biography of Carpeaux, which was in turn published by GV's friend Paul Iribe.

than 100 pounds. Though born in France, she was Italian, and Sanz, one of my friends who knew everyone who was anyone in Paris, told me that although she went by the name of Esmerelda in real life, her stage name was Esmée.

I had of course from time to time known dancers whose rank and talents were more imagined than actual, but I had never had the honour of knowing a real dancer, and in the few words I exchanged with Miss Esmerelda, I was surprised by this young woman's grace, level-headedness, poise and spirituality. I later learned the reason for these qualities. The classical dancer is a being whose existence is bound up with the toughest, most difficult and most demanding of all women's activities. The four members of the Academy of Music and Dance among us were women formed by the gymnastics of grace - and from this daily effort, certain virtues were born: candour, a little pride, unfailing courage, a passion for beauty, and to crown it all, a sort of lofty humility.

Encountering these priestesses for the first time, I found in them the strict discipline I admired in my professional mechanic friends, leavened by music and an extraordinary musical memory. After an hour of humdrum tangos, I invited the assembled company back to Boulevard Exelmans. By midnight, we were gathered there around an improvised supper. When the time for leave-taking suddenly intruded, I accompanied Esmerelda home. The address she gave me turned out to be her mother's, and rather a long way away. I did my best not to be importunate, and with some difficulty managed to arrange a rendezvous four days later, on January 2nd. We were to dine again - at the rue Royale, naturally.

I had only been in the restaurant foyer for a moment when I saw my guest arrive in the company of a friend, another dancer at the Opéra. I installed my terpsichoreans and suggested a menu. The friend of 'smiler' must have been the mischief-maker of the ballet company. They announced that they had been dying of thirst ever since leaving class that morning. I had no idea what to offer them, but I saw our maître d'hôtel, Jean, expertly place two glasses of beer on our table.

With the gusto of a hard-drinking market porter after a long day's work, my two priestesses downed these draughts with eyes half-closed, and, with a synchronicity that pleased me greatly, they both unaffectedly drew the backs of their hands across their lips and let out a great sigh.

Then it was a matter of the menu. Although I don't exactly remember the succession of dishes that appeared on our table, I have never before seen two young ladies of such delicate appearance eat with such healthy appetites. This they explained to me:

"Our voracity surprises you, monsieur. But after slaving away all morning and suffering the thousand deaths of a lesson, all 84 dancers of the *corps de ballet* drink as we have and eat as we do. Perhaps you've heard that frequenting classical dancers is a costly business? Worry not. We don't indulge in haute couture - indeed, we know how to handle a needle ourselves - but it must be admitted that nourishing a rat, a quadrille, a *petit* or *grand sujet*,[10] is of necessity a ruinous thing. No diet problems for us. We could pillage a *pâtisserie*, devour a veal calf, stuff ourselves with sugar or bread and still remain as thin as rakes. But in a week's holiday, we can put on 10 kilos, which disappears just as quickly when we return..."

This healthy appetite only made them more attractive to me. Women who are prissy eaters have always bored me with their misplaced delicacy. I was already on a precariously slippery slope...

---

10) The ranks of achievement in classical ballet, from novice to leading dancer.

My guests threw themselves back into a repeat performance. That evening, settling myself into the stalls among the season ticket holders, I recognised the dazzling smile of December 30th among the tutus of *Faust*. She really was exceptionally beautiful, especially her eyes. I waited for her in rue Meyerbeer and drove her back to the maternal home, near the offices of *Le Matin*.[11]

The question arose of another rendezvous, which I was granted. The following week, to my delight, I dined with Esmée alone. The dinner continued until late, and I suggested returning to the rue Poissonnière. Arriving near the place Vendôme, I emboldened myself to suggest to my guest a detour to boulevard Exelmans. The reply wasn't immediate; I was very politely asked to drive around the column to give her time to think. The first circuit was followed by a second. We discussed the matter, but I was making progress. By the end of the sixth lap, only one of my hands was doing the driving. She consented to the detour...

At boulevard Exelmans, December's reserve evaporated. When I drove my beautiful victim back home much later that night, the slope had become so slippery that braking was quite impossible, front or rear...

It was to lead me to much happiness in the company of a quite exceptional human being. In my life I have known three Italian women, two very reserved English girls and a woman who must have hailed from central Europe. The Italians all left me with unforgettable memories. Certain regions of Italy have given us incomparable joys. It's not inconceivable that this utter perfection harks back to the virtues of antiquity.

---

11) In the boulevard Poissonnière - a quarter GV knew well from when he first moved to Paris to find work as an architect in 1903, staying with his school friend Claudius Genevrier, who was on the right wing daily's editorial staff.

TORPÉDO 4 PLACES — "SÉRIE SPÉCIALE"

Esmée, though French and Parisian, was born of Bolognese parents. In my workshops at Issy-les-Moulineaux, I had workers from Etruria and Tuscany, and their qualities were all similar to those of this young woman whom I was to render both very happy and very sad, and who, having given me her heart, never once claimed it back.

At Issy-les-Moulineaux, the factory was ticking over with no major problems. Our order book was full. I had enough of a breathing space to allow me a few diversions.

Passing judgement on a motor car was the extent of my knowledge before 1918. My subsequent observations, progressively refined by their sheer number, by many incidents, endless machining difficulties and innumerable comparisons, had rendered me hypersensitive. In short, the car I aspired to making had nothing to do with the usual confections. Aerodynamic considerations concerned me not one jot: 20 years of aviation had allowed me to integrate the requisite forms.

But the mechanical side troubled me - the crudeness of internal combustion engines, with their clattering starter motors, booming exhaust and sheer inflexibility. The clutch seemed to me (and still does) a kind of mechanical confidence trick, and despite everything that has been conceived or done of to improve it, I still haven't come to terms with the gearbox and its controls, its noisiness, inflexibility and mechanical inefficiency. In a word, I saw myself about to undertake a serious crusade, and prepared a detailed plan.

Among my personal ironmongery that cluttered up an area of the factory, I kept what remained of three steam cars, one of which was American. The rebuilding of these antiques allowed me to construct a practically unmodernised chassis that I was able to try out in April 1920. Having completely forgotten the marvels of steam, my first trip (despite a malfunctioning boiler) was a delight. To a clientèle determined to endure the most dreadful mechanical problems, it was of course impossible to offer even an infinitely perfected version of the vehicle I drove round our usual test track that April. But the machine I had resurrected, modernised of course with proper steering and brakes, and with acceptable suspension and roadholding, proved quite remarkable.

Obviously, the boiler had to be fired, a less simple operation than might imagine. Alcohol, fuel oil and finally petrol were involved, all accompanied by appalling smoke. When the boilers were eventually hot, regulated and fully operational, you had to wait patiently for ten or fifteen minutes before the monster could start off properly.

When the pressure and temperature gauges and the levels were acceptable, the car was finally ready to depart. No overtaxed batteries, no Bendix capable of waking a whole neighbourhood in winter (despite so-called automatic starters): one simple movement, forward or reverse. One single control: the admission of steam, after which this best of machines would move off with magical flexibility, without perceptible noise, oil fumes, vibration, clutch, or foot and hand manipulation. A touch of the inlet control, and thundering acceleration would propel the ensemble forwards, still silently, and still with that incomparable smoothness, that absolute impossibility of guessing the number of cylinders.

No first gear, no reverse to be groped for, no second, no third, no overdrive. A machine always fit to tackle any obstacle, to climb whatever gradient at top speed. In brief, a marvel - alas unusable for the legion of clodhoppers who talk cars, pass judgement and wish to own a 'Cougar' or some such...

This was the perfection I hoped to achieve with the benefit of what I had learned in 20 years of tinkering about. The steam engine has an indisputable advantage over any internal combustion unit: its power is not limited by capacity, only by mechanical resistance. This means that a steam engine can supply 100 horsepower, for example, at 10rpm just as easily as it can at 100. In a word, it automatically solves the vexatious problem of variable torque. The combustion engine, whose ascendancy is due to its astonishing thermal efficiency, only supplies full power at certain engine speeds, and that power disappears as soon as the rpm rises above or falls below the peak of its lamentable power curve.

Let's not fool ourselves, the motor car is the realm of the artisan and tinkerer, and very heaven for show-offs. As with most human endeavours, habit is the driving force. The manufacturer, his thinking occluded by a single idea, is insulated from foresight. He constructs the 'monster' and puts in train all the resources at his disposal to establish the product. When his efforts succeed, he immerses himself immediately in numbers, that is to say what he believes to be profit. Only the test of time can put an end to his undertaking.

The scooter phenomenon is a striking case in point. Despite wheels whose tiny diameter minimises the gyroscopic momentum *without which two-wheelers cannot function*, this extraordinary Italian device literally swamped the market. Huge factories of technicians who ought to have known better constructed thousands of these murderous machines until the day when insurers, who don't take risk lightly, declared scooters to be the most dangerous of all forms of transport. There are thousands of similar tales. The first monster is born. Riddled with faults as it inevitably is, common sense and the simplest technical analysis dictate a redesign to rectify the flaws of the original. To no good purpose, of course - the initial mistakes are never tackled. They are accommodated, and this tendency to compromise applies in all things.

The first internal combustion engines were started by turning a crank handle which was not only self-evidently dangerous but required both physical effort and a considerable knack. This inconvenience had to be eliminated. The simplest solution seemed to be to replace the starting handle with an electrical device which would act as both starter motor and a generator. But electric starting was an uncertain business in the heroic days, so the crank handle remained. Coming up with an electrical device with a crank handle was too much to expect! The tinkerers tinkered away for a long time, and their tinkerings led to a toothed flywheel against which a starter motor pinion would engage. The fact is, under the influence of a thousand ignoramuses, this reluctance to reconsider the starting handle condemned millions of cars to start with a totally unacceptable amount of noise, all the while forcing upon them two superposed electrical devices, together with all the attached impedimenta by way of belts, pulleys and their well-known inconveniences.

From 1922 onwards, Voisin delivered all its cars of whatever capacity with a device that was silent, unique and functioned indefinitely.[12] 65,000 cars[13] left Issy-les-Moulineaux equipped with this unquestionably perfect mechanism, but 'modern' cars still make an unholy racket when they start, and country garages make a living from replacing electrical equipment.

A clutch is a delicate device, requiring a considerable knack to control small manoeuvres. It is inherently fragile and costly to replace. Yet it still lives on today, accommodated by costly and fragile contrivances that don't correct all its faults.

---

12) GV refers here to models introduced after this date, when the C4 was announced. All variants of the four-litre Voisin (which remained in production until 1928) were equipped with conventional starter motors.

13) A typographical error. In the first volume of *Men, Women and 10,000 Kites*, GV variously quotes a total production of 25,000 and 27,200 cars (and 10,400 aeroplanes); Charles Dolfuss wrote of 17,100 in his 1975 essay for *Icare*; in 1991, Courteault put the figure at "no more than 15,000". However, the most informed estimate of the total number of Voisin cars made (excluding Biscuter production in Spain) is in the order of 7,000 units.

As for the gearbox, after 60 years of idiotic solutions from the Fouillaron belt[14] and so-called automatic gearchanges right through to the shameful American monstrosity of the so-called hydraulic box, the problem remains the same as it was in 1900: an iron bar adorned with a piece of plastic shifts cogs machined at the cost of a king's ransom, and this mechanism has the temerity to accommodate itself to a power curve like the bell of a village church!

I shall say nothing of what technicians called the transmission drive train, but it seems that all human stupidity had conspired to resolve a problem that a village idiot would have dealt with by eliminating the lot.

I had of course very big ambitions when I began my design. But I took the bull by the horns and tried hard to find solutions. It nevertheless proved impossible to carry out my plans, and the enormous personal investment of time and effort involved would in any case have yielded only marginal improvements for use in our products thereafter.

I decided from the beginning that my engine's starter and dynamo would be a single unit, and I designed a crankshaft-driven dynamo-cum-starter.[15] Electrical devices had always been inaccessible. The dynamo/starter was equipped at the front with a radial commutator which could be instantly removed without tools. Automotive electricians warned me of problems, but my electric devices are still functioning with their original parts after 30 years of use...

14) Fouillaron cars were fitted with infinitely variable automatic transmission between 1900 and 1914.

15) See patent 510.810 (February 1920)

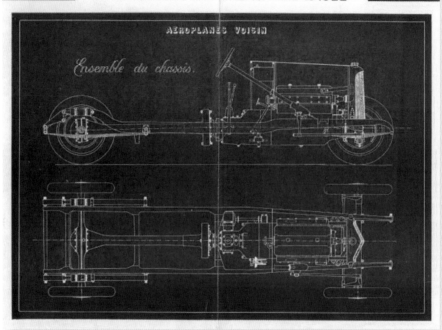

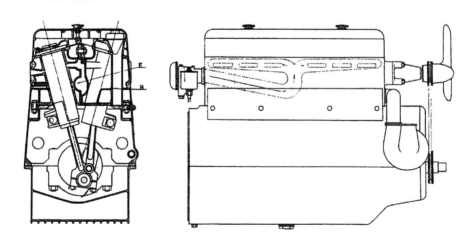

From the starter, I moved on to the engine. To achieve unprecedented flexibility, I settled on a V12 of four litres capacity.[16] I expected wonders from this machine. Although there was no such thing as science fiction in 1920, I still believe 40 years later that my 12-cylinder could profitably feature in a modern children's history of engineering...

This water-cooled twelve consisted of three castings, in aluminium of course: the crankcase and right and left cylinder blocks. All the induction pipes, water passages, oilways and wiring conduits were integrally cast, so that none were visible from outside.[17] A single carburettor was at the rear, in line with the crankshaft. The clutch consisted of two opposed turbines running in oil, with an electromagnet coming into play at the end of the clutch travel to lock the turbines together. This clutch could be slipped for an hour without stress or any significant rise in temperature.

The gearbox had only two forward speeds and reverse. I had four-wheel brakes of course - actuated by compressed air, as in modern commercial vehicles. In a car, this complexity is still of no interest.

I began my first design studies in December 1919; on April 20th 1920, my 12-cylinder was ready for its first trials. In any big factory, you always get troublemakers who take it upon themselves to question everything that management wants to undertake. The appearance in 1920 of a car with a 12-cylinder engine and the innovations that accompanied it provoked endless criticism from within. By the time the prototype was ready, I learned that my staff were divided into two factions: the 'noes' who were betting on the complete failure of my project, and the 'ayes', who expected miracles.

---

16) Homer nods. The capacity of the experimental V12 in the radically innovative C2 was 7,237cc.

17) See patent 526.075 (October 1920).

Albert Descorme *(sic)* ran a book on the wagers, and I discovered that the 'noes' were to treat the 'ayes' to a lavish dinner if the car proved capable of undertaking our usual test route from Paris to Cannes and back. The pessimists, in other words, required an untried and highly original creation to undertake a journey of some 2,000 kilometres.

Preliminary tests revealed little. I soon realised that neither my 12-cylinder engine nor the other innovations had quite lived up to my expectations. I had clearly not succeeded in creating a steam car powered by an internal combustion engine. But as a prototype, it was nevertheless quite respectable.

We could hardly extract more than 80 horsepower from our perfectly silent twelve. The electrics were a success, the air brakes worked well enough, and my clutch (though much too expensive) had many fine qualities. Logically, I should have embarked on a rigorous development programme and then abandoned this costly experiment. Misplaced pride however inclined me towards the Paris-Cannes circuit, because I wanted to teach a lesson to the malcontents who had wormed their way into our factory.

At two in the morning of the 25th April 1920, I set out for Cannes followed by a fully equipped support car carrying my faithful team from the *laboratoire*. The first 300 kilometres took only four hours, reaching Châlons-sur-Saône towards 6 a.m. At that very moment, the air brake compressor failed, leaving me with nothing but the handbrake. Having to dismantle the compressor in the shelter of a hedge beside the left bank of the Saône should have taught us the folly of our endeavour, but I was determined to complete the route. I took out the spark plug from the number 12 cylinder and connected it up to the compressed air tank. Although we had lost two hours, this one cylinder proved sufficient allow a certain amount of braking.

We were approaching Grenoble at about 1 o'clock when the clutch failed. A bronze bush had seized, and I decided to dismantle it near the village of Côte Saint-André. It was a nightmarish procedure. Its position made access extremely difficult. I started the engine, and injected paraffin by syringe into the seized component.

The bush in question freed itself after a few minutes, but its shaft was still so hot that it vaporised the paraffin. Out of the blue, there was an almighty explosion in the turbine casing which blew out the oil in both housings, blinding me and covering me with a film of very hot black liquid.

But the bush was free. The unit was reassembled by the end of the afternoon, and I sent André Lefebvre to Côte Saint-André to organise a much-needed meal. When I arrived at the hotel where we were expected, I was dripping with oil, my hair and eyebrows singed off by the explosion. The hotelier invited me to bathe and change and it was dusk by the time our 12-cylinder was ready to depart again. Sleep was out of the question. Miraculously, the night passed without incident, and exhausted but happy, we finally arrived in the sunshine of Cannes. We had covered our thousand kilometres in 22 hours!

Once the telegrams had been duly despatched, the *laboratoire* team slept for 12 hours. Two days' rest gave us enough time to repair and modify the compressor, and the V12 set off on the return journey, which was accomplished without further problem in 16 hours 35 minutes.

The 'noes' having been thus confounded, the resulting celebratory dinners and lunches lasted over ten days. But once the financial reckonings had been made, my dream machine seemed no more than an idiotically futile exercise.

Nevertheless, our 12-cylinder passed to the testing stage.[18] The electrics were immediately productionised with great success. The basic crankcase arrangement was adopted for our 10CV, then on our 13CV 6-cylinder models. Our efforts hadn't been entirely wasted. Three years later, we were to offer our clientèle a Voisin sleeve valve V12 well before the Rolls Royce Phantom, and which could be compared favourably with the creation of the most famous make in the world.[19]

In the 40 years that have passed since my adventure with the 12-cylinder, I have of course seen enormous progress in road transport. However, I again constructed another steam car in 1940 - a light van we used constantly, fuelled by a stock of old timbers. It was powered by a compound twin-cylinder steam engine I had designed in a few wecks,[20] with distribution via a sleeve sliding outside the cylinder. With seven or eight kilos of boiler pressure, this double action machine produced between 15 and 20 horsepower - from a total capacity of around 200cc! A toy that, including lubricant, weighed a mere 19 kilos!

This van made my heart leap the first time I took it out. I rediscovered the marvels I had known 20 years earlier. The ease of driving, the prodigious flexibility, the thundering acceleration, all the miracles were contained in this little truck which was only a make-do imposed by lack of petrol.

---

18) A second prototype was built. Although the 30-degree V12 remained essentially the same, it differed in several ways from the first car: it reverted to right-hand drive, with a conventional clutch and gearbox and semi-elliptic front springs in place of the complex transmission and transverse front leaf system (January 1921 patent 529.972) of the lhd original, and a new type of rear suspension with horizontal shock absorbers actuated by rocker arms (September 1921 patent 541.768).

19) Voisin's production V12 was not in fact offered until 1929 (which was nevertheless six years before the PIII); the extent to which the Issy unit's modest 100bhp output compared favourably with Elliott's 7.3 litre R-R V12 is of course debatable.

20) See 1944 patents 903.657, 905.553 & 905.554.

It's difficult to foresee the future of motorised transport. Nuclear energy seems to have credible potential. Gunpowder, which caused such an immense military revolution, was originally just a fantastical smoke machine. In the naval battles of the *Musée de la Marine*, entire squadrons are made to disappear in opaque clouds. The smoke that accompanied each shot in those days provided an easy target for return fire, yet within 100 years, generals were once again confounded, by the advent of smokeless powder.

It will be the same for atomic fission. In less than 20 years, the fallout from atomic bombs will have disappeared like the smoke from gunpowder. It will no longer be a matter of petrol and petrol stations. The pumps will disappear over a few months, and the energy required by ultra-powerful cars will be contained in a sugar lump. Then, steam power (not necessarily water vapour) will have a good chance of propelling our cars, and the drivers in 2000 will certainly be liberated from our outmoded starters, our gearboxes, incendiary combustions that require constant refuelling and so many other freakish notions.

As for 'styling', the refuge of the charlatan, it will have long since disappeared, definitively crushed by the irresistible imperative of FUNCTION.

Chapter III

I discovered while reading the evening paper that same year that a lot of redundant submarine chasers were being auctioned off. Prompted by memories of youthful boat trips, embellished by the passage of time, my ever-present daemons of escape prompted me to make an offer.

For 12,000 francs I became the owner of a very nice vessel. My friend Noël accompanied me to Cherbourg to take delivery. Furnished with innumerable authorisations, passes and complicated receipts, I entered the naval base and saw a boat lying forlornly at the far end of the dock in a terrible state.

It had to be removed from the naval establishment, but the innards of my vessel lay scattered in disarray along the quay. I then made the acquaintance of two sailors who were approaching demobilisation. They were naval mechanics, and I told them of my predicament. Announcing that they would be returning to civilian life the very next month, these two resourceful chaps offered to refit my engines (with which they were thoroughly familiar).

I did a deal with my new blue-collar associates. The elder, Letournel, was then and still is a prodigious mechanic, and after many voyages and a huge amount of work, we remain firm friends. The younger was called Mouchard. Less able than Letournel, he was nevertheless an excellent professional and a good sailor besides. 18 years later, he was to vanish in an affair of the heart so mysterious that I never quite understood what happened.

GV's motor launch was one of the US-built 'Cinderellas of the Fleet', which were only three years old at the time. Roosevelt ordered the new class of submarine chaser to stem losses off the Eastern seaboard in 1916. Heavy demand for steel led to the vessels being made of wood, and of a size that could be built in small yards: 110' (33.5m) long, with a 16' (4.9m) beam. Powered by a brace of 220hp petrol engines from the Standard Motor Construction Co. of New Jersey, 355 of these 85-tonners were constructed from March 1917, of which 50 were consigned to the French Navy. The quoted maximum speed of the SC class was around 18-21 knots, but without the armour plating and an array of weaponry that included 3'' canons, heavy machine guns and a depth charge projector, GV's conversion must have been considerably faster.

I returned to Paris and received a telegram from Cherbourg the following month. The recommissioning was complete; Letournel and Mouchard were available. Enthused by the prospect of sailing once again, I removed my vessel from the naval base and prepared to sail her down to Meulan, where I planned to have her fitted out.

She was between 30 and 35 metres long with a beam of nearly 6 metres, if memory serves me right. I was aware of the nautical qualities of my 'greyhound of the seas'. The mechanical elements were magnificent, undamaged by their time in naval service. The three Standard 250hp six-cylinder engines were connected directly to three propellers, with no clutch. Starting forwards or backwards was obtained by reversing the distribution cams and by a large reservoir of compressed air fed by an independent compressor. The remainder was in keeping. The tanks held 5,000 litres of fuel, and I filled them up two days after arriving at Cherbourg. Being duty free, this was quite affordable.

On Tuesday - at midnight, as we needed high tide to leave our beaching strand - I took the helm and checked the Chatburn[1] (*sic*). My two mechanics were in the engine room, and in order to minimise the risks of navigating in unknown waters from Cherbourg to the mouth of the Seine at night, I asked for the services of a pilot. On cue, the right and left engines burst into life. Alleviated of all its military impedimenta (having left 10 or 12 tons of assorted ironmongery back on the quay), my boat, with its 500 horses, rose up like a water ski, and we were out of Cherbourg harbour in a few seconds. Frightened by this blind force propelling my hundred tons into the night, I slowed down. We were at sea. The sky was impenetrably black. I checked my compass, gave my course to the pilot and handed him the helm. The engines were a comforting sight, and ran faultlessly.

---

1) The wheelhouse engine order telegraph (as made by Chadburn of Liverpool).

Half an hour later, the moon rose. I went down to my cabin to lie down for a while. I had only been asleep for a few minutes when the engine note changed. I opened my eyes. The moon whose rays I had observed a little earlier shining through a porthole had moved by 90 degrees! I shot into the wheelhouse. My pilot had never used a compass. Indicating the lighthouse of Vire ahead, he assured me we were looking at the lighthouse of Le Havre, whereas it in fact signals a bank of rocks near the coast! I ordered the imbecile to his cabin and changed course 90 degrees West.

It was just in time. Our position was confirmed when I heard the sound of breakers immediately astern. This was in June. In the light of dawn, I spotted Deauville on the horizon to my right. The entry of the Seine estuary worried me. I ran up flags to signal for a pilot and stopped engines. The pilot of course never came. A light freighter loomed up on our left, apparently heading for the mouth of the river. I waited, and followed in its wake. The Seine was congested with big ships on their way to Le Havre, never deviating from their familiar course. One had to navigate by guesswork, and I was constantly expecting to run aground. Fortunately, we never did.

We finally arrived at Rouen in the morning. I had to disembark the moronic pilot I had taken on, and the quays were cluttered with manoeuvring barges. After passing under a bridge, I soon found myself the other side of the town!

My engines which functioned so marvellously were quite incapable of slow speeds. The banks of the river were rushing past at a hellish rate, and I had to steer between two quays very close to each other. A dangerous ebb tide pushed me towards one of the piers of the bridge I had just passed. Miraculously, I managed to negotiate the bend without mishap.

Now following the current, I turned a second time, still at undiminished pace, and let off my fellow by the bridge with a huge sigh of relief. A moment later, I was in the Seine.

I cut one of my engines and passed through my first lock. On a single engine, my barely controllable craft threw up veritable tidal waves, which were greeted with insults and threats by the riverside residents, lightermen, walkers and curious passers by.

In the afternoon, we were moored at Vétheuil, in the Seine-et-Oise, in front of *Le Talus,* where I had been seduced by the charms of the misses Bernet 12 years earlier. I had bought this charming house from Victor Margueritte[2], and went there on Sundays in summer. That day my wife was waiting for me, expecting great things from my new acquisition. With luck on our side, we had realised our plans for escape and we hadn't even considered what to name our ship.

We agreed on *Ariel,*[3] in remembrance of Shelley. My two mechanics completed a few jobs on board, and eight days later *Ariel* was berthed at Meulan in front of the shipyards that were to turn her into a modern yacht. I expected the refit to be completed by September, and that my new vessel would spend the winter in Cannes harbour. Man proposes, but God disposes.

---

2) The novelist **Victor Margueritte** (1866-1942) was married to the sister of GV's wife Adrienne, and became famous after the scandal surrounding the publication of *La Garçonne* in 1922 and his subsequent expulsion from the Legion of Honour. Selling more than a million copies, the novella's androgynous protagonist was a defining influence on the styles and mores of the *années folles,* notably for inspiring the vogue for women to wear the short bobs, cloche hats and trousers. The house in Vétheuil was on the site of an old château in rue des Fraîches Femmes; GV's nephew Michel Collet compared it to the Kennedy compound at Hyannisport, containing as it did several houses for accommodating GV's extended family during the holidays.

3) Ominously so, in view of the fact that Shelley lost his life in the ketch in question after being rammed by a band of felucca while sailing home to the Bay of Lenci from a visit to Byron in 1822. GV would have known this saga from the (now discredited) biography that first won André Maurois fame in 1923: *Ariel, ou la vie de Shelley.*

The Almighty upset my plans, and I was once more plunged into impossible mechanical problems. Having neglected the Minotaur for nautical pleasures for a few weeks, it awaited me, talons extended, at Issy-les-Moulineaux.

In 1920, and for a long time thereafter, motor cars were constructed in two parts. On one hand, the chassis, including the engine, transmission, radiator, bonnet and part of the scuttle; on the other, clumsily bolted onto the chassis, the coachwork.

The body rested on chassis rails, themselves relics of the carriages used by idle royalty in the days when the monarch's litter lay on two tree trunks parallel to the direction of travel. The axles that bore the wheels were fixed across the chassis rails. The advent of powerful and costly machines had not remotely modified these biblical arrangements. Our first chassis had been bodied by Kellner, probably one of the world's premier coachbuilders. But the construction of these great crates produced monstrosities whose completely unacceptable weight threatened to ruin the chassis we made.

In a word, our bare chassis was a brilliant success. But as our clients lost no time in telling us, when crushed under 700 kilos of timber, useless bits of ironmongery, crossmembers, uprights and all the upholstery on top, our Voisin struggled like an overburdened pony.

It was impossible to make the motorist of 1920 understand the question of weight. My own salesmen (because I had had to succumb to the formation of a so-called sales department) had, in my absence, hit upon the idea of entering one of our standard cars in various competitions.

The first Voisin *Laboratoire*, as described opposite. The doorless fabric body featured a windscreen that was fully retractable into the scuttle. At least two were built.

This monstrosity was well advanced, in the form of a torpedo to be painted bright red, with an unusual abundance of nickel plating. I had this aberration dismantled and set about creating, over a few days, an ensemble that would shine in other ways than by its decorative accessories.

France having just emerged from the war, motoring skills had been highly developed by intensive practice on all fronts. On their return to hearth and home, all the drivers, all the barely qualified military mechanics, dreamed only of motoring exploits, and every village in France organised motor races on an almost weekly basis.

It wasn't possible to establish a proper circuit. The road network was one of the country's great war casualties, and was in no state to be taken lightly. Nevertheless, larger towns possessed a steep hill that admirably suited improvised events known as hillclimbs. Road menders would patch up the surface, tarring it here and there, and the Sillygoosington Hillclimb was deemed ready to receive the monsters. These weren't particularly fearsome - the big manufacturers, fearful of getting egg on their faces, initially abstained from these competitions altogether.

But there were among the number of entrants some very reckless people. Two young men, both mechanics, had for example fitted a 200hp Hispano Suiza aero engine to some chassis or other. This unit, astonishing for its time, was not only admirably designed, but weighed a mere 180 kilos ready to go. These amateurs' car was therefore the No.1 competitor, and we had to think very carefully about how we were going to beat it.

I chose one of our best standard engines and transformed it as best I could, and when we put it on the dynamometer it gave nearly 100 horsepower at 2,950rpm. I then designed a body - a tapering hull three metres long, 90cms wide, containing two wicker seats.

... et sur Voisin montant Gaillon à 120 Km à l'h. Record

POST OFFICE TELEGRAPHS.

PARIS 48498 31 10 21H32 :
= MONSIEUR ARTAULT DRIVING TWENTY TWO POINT FOUR VOISIN
FOUR SEATED CAR BEAT ALL TOURING CAR RECORDS FOR FAMOUS
GAILLON HILL CLIMB TODAY OCTOBER TENTHE =   CURTIS :

CURLANATH PICCY LONDON

CARBURATEUR ZENITH

Rougier sur Voisin au grand virage dans la course de côte de Limonest
gagnant de toutes catégories tourisme et course à 102 Km à l'heure (7.5.22)

82

My friend Piat, a magician with wood, drew on elements of our 1917 triplane[4] that he knew so well. He constructed a series of light hoops connected by a lattice, and the result was pasted up with linen fabric.

This masterpiece of ingenuity weighed only 19 kilos. Our first test was at the Gaillon hillclimb, where the car, weighing about 700 kilos in full trim, literally flew. The crucial coefficient of empennage allowed us to take the most feared corners flat out.

The Voisin 18CV began its racing career in 1920, competing against the Hispano-engined chassis, among others. He started first, as we were racing against the clock in alphabetical order. His start was impressive, but the hill in question had a reverse camber bend, and the Hispano disappeared into the bushes, never to be seen again. The trophy was ours a few minutes later. After that, we hardly drew breath. We were assailed by race organisers, and every Sunday I had to attend such runs. Our car performed well, and at the Côte de Limonest, near Lyon, our time was never beaten.[5]

These simple cars provided excellent publicity in the regions. The clientèle of budding hillclimbers immediately ordered replicas of our much-garlanded racer, but as we could hardly offer buyers canvas bodies with wicker seats, I developed what was to become the C5 from our improvised car.

4) The most imposing Voisin of all, the 38-metre twin-fuselage triplane bomber *J.Benoist-L.Mijduant* was built in only eight weeks in 1915, powered by four 270hp Salmson radials mounted back to back on the central wing - the first four-engined aircraft to fly in France. A photograph of GV beside this giant machine appears in the introduction.

5) This challenging 3.7 kilometre course was climbed in 2 minutes 12 seconds on May 28th 1922 by Henri Rougier, who went on to win the touring car class at La Turbie, Gaillon, Pic Montaigu and Les Alpilles. Artault triumphed in the hillclimbs at Egremont, Chartres and Evreux as well as Gaillon in 1920, and at Poix and Gaillon the following year. Paul Bablot drove a 4-litre to victory at Mont Ventoux in 1921, and at Allauch in 1922; Cabaillot won at Vigen, Malchamps and Malmedy, and Gaudermann at Vimille, Boulogne and Planfoy. The 4-litre also distinguished itself at many track and endurance events, especially where fuel consumption was a criterion.

Rudolph Valentino au bois de Boulogne sur son torpédo Voisin C5

new-york 23

Lower and more powerful than its C1 and C3 predecessors, the C5 was introduced in 1923.

The slender streamlined body was too long to park in normal spaces, so I shortened it. The seating allowed room for four, and our first sports models were literally torn from our hands by this niche clientèle.

The C5 evolved our bodywork skills. Coachbuilders persisted with their ponderous creations, grotesque assemblages of oak beams and steel panels hammered into shape. These monsters of several hundred kilos were of course entirely made by hand. Skilled panelbeaters took a sheet of steel, cut it and shaped it to the desired form, rounded, twisted, folded, unfolded, embossed. This superhuman work of art was obtained by successive deformations, stretching or otherwise compromising the metal. The panelbeater was a unique magician, and the perfection of his work has always flabbergasted me. How could one waste so much skill, tenacity and effort to no functional purpose?

Voisin only ever made bodies entirely from aluminium, and a few of our creations remain unscathed after 40 years of continuous use. The fragility argument cannot therefore be invoked. Why aren't car bodies made solely of light alloy, which does not oxidise and is therefore of extraordinary longevity?

The answer is simple. Carriages were made entirely of wood, and their various components slowly evolved into set forms. But when the motor industry underwent its great expansion, there could be no question of assembling elaborate Louis XVI panelling: there wasn't enough wood in all the forests of France. Manufacturers therefore turned to steel, but lacking the courage or the ingenuity to imagine new ways of using a material that in no way resembled wood, they faithfully reproduced in metal what cart makers in the old days had constructed from trunks of oak or ash. The panelbeater was replaced by presses, formers and punches whose enormous cost could only be defrayed by producing thousands of increasingly unsellable objects.

Then as now, informed commentators viewed the factory-bodied C5 torpedo as one of the finest cars of its era.

Aluminium is not suited to this form of construction. The use of this light metal requires a discernment that is no longer demanded from our technicians, who just want an easy life, and so coachbuilders persist in constructing doors with frames, beams and panels made of a material three times heavier than aluminium. These monuments to idleness, ignorance and technical stupidity rust away at a terrifying rate, because only the visible part of a car is painted with any care, leaving the underside and the angles where the metal has been stretched thin to corrode away.

Our C5, bodied entirely in aluminium and realised in 'developable' surfaces, was of course a light car. Its shape was acceptably aerodynamic, and it could achieve 140kph fully laden. The acceleration was impressive, and the roadholding passable - it had been improved by significantly shortening the chassis so as to optimise the centre of pressure. Sadly, the first models delivered had one intolerable vice: the steering, although agreeable enough on very good roads, became pretty much unacceptable on poor surfaces.

It was obviously impossible to suspend production until an effective remedy was found to this problem, which provoked a violent reaction in the steering wheel - violent enough in some cases to injure the driver's hands. I had to find an easy and inexpensive way of suppressing this vice at all costs. I despaired, baffled by fruitless attempts to rectify the fault, until an incident revealed the cause of our torment.

One morning Mazoyer, one of our best testers, came to fetch me in my garret to put a theory to me. An excellent driver, whose observations were always pertinent, this expert put me at the wheel of a C5 and with no further explanation, suggested that I drive round our usual circuit...

Right: Although this particular C5 (by Gaston Grümmer, to Bunau-Varilla patents) is clearly not the heavily bodied coupé to which GV so strongly objected, it nevertheless provides an instructive contrast to the sternly geometric lightweight factory saloon in the signature 'prismatic' style seen on the following page.

Below: a C5 chassis outside the factory annexe

This particular car, whose chassis was of strictly standard specification, suffered no kick-back at all. However, with careful attention, you could discern a phenomenon that we couldn't explain. We had to discover the reason for this fortuitous modification to our machine. I only noticed one thing: that this C5 was not bodied by Voisin, but by some Levallois coachbuilder or other. Like a glass-fronted wardrobe with japanned leather hood, it had two thick doors weighing some 100 kilos; to those proficient in jujitsu, they allowed awkward access to four seats whose size would have suited a monkey.

I weighed this marvel. Despite its modest interior dimensions, the body tipped the scales at 500 kilos! By removing the doors, seats, arm rests, sound deadening, carpet and hood, I lost nearly 200 kilos, thereby reducing it to the loaded weight of our own car.

Still no kickback. But with Mazoyer driving, I sat in the rear, where it seemed to me that the floor of this extraordinary coachwork, made up of loose tongue-and-groove boards, was moving diagonally.

I had the flexible coachwork on this puzzling chassis replaced by a Voisin body. Hardly had I left the annexe when, slowly traversing the little ditch that remained from the old perimeter wall of the drill ground, violent kick-back tore the steering wheel from my hands.

Mazoyer then took my place and we embarked on the test route. There was no point in driving ten kilometres - the steering kickback was intolerable. I then had the Levallois coachwork dismantled. How could a body like ours provoke such reactions when a wooden body suppressed them, or at least made them acceptable?

The statigraphic method was required. I had our chassis fitted with the bare floor of a Voisin body, a sheet of 3mm aluminium bolted to the chassis rails. I tried it; the kickback remained.

I removed the C5 floor, and it disappeared. I had the Levallois body refitted once more, but with two sturdy diagonal cross-members fixed beneath the floor to eliminate the longitudinal deflexions of the right chassis rail in relation to the left. The kick-back returned, but I could produce it at will by tightening or loosening the tensioners of my two diagonals.

The result of our experiments was clear: the floor of our Voisin C5 bodies, being carefully bolted to the chassis rails, prevented the chassis from flexing diagonally; so evidently our C5 chassis, perfectly rigid vertically, was deforming itself horizontally when a steered wheel encountered any violent shock. I measured this deformation, unhindered as it was by rubber engine or gearbox mountings; at high speed, the diagonal distortion was in the order of 15 millimetres.

To get out of this impasse, we had to find an inexpensive and rapid solution that permitted a degree of relative freedom to the front axle in the horizontal plane. On the spot I drew a device consisting of two very short spring hangers that I installed at the front, and fitted two opposing coil springs, hardly visible, on the rear spring hangers of the front axle.

The effect of this arrangement was spectacular. Our steering lost very little of its precision, but the kick-back disappeared once and for all. The modification could be fitted to our existing C5s in two hours. Our competitors were nonplussed...

I did of course take out a patent,[6] and a few days after this worthless precaution (unless one pursues ruinously expensive litigation), the excellent Latil company, which also suffered similar kick-back, applied to us for a license. This patent was I think the only one ever to earn me anything...

6) GV applied for the patent late in the model's life, in January 1927 (627.953); with their twinned coil springs, these sliding trunnions became known as *jumelles* (binoculars).

Above: Henri Rougier in the Paris-Nice C5, en route to winning the touring car class at Gaillon.

Below: serial Swedish Voisin owner Ohlsson racing his new C5 early in 1924.

I was nevertheless confirmed in the opinion I had held for 10 years, ever since the day the ghastly shimmy on my old Lorraine-Dietrich had disappeared when a random piece of flint lodged itself in one of its kingpins. The lesson of this escapade was easy to draw: *the steering axis must pass through the centre of gravity of its wheels, which must in turn coincide with the centre of the contact patch; when this arrangement is impossible to realise, the axis must at all costs be made to approach this centre as closely as possible.*

My C5 axles were thus equipped. I could change nothing major, nor could I obtain this coincidence of axes and centres which I knew to be indispensable. But, by a series of small modifications, I gained a few millimetres in the position of our axles, and when, a little later, we built the 13CV six-cylinder that was such a commercial and technical success, I could offer our clients the finest steering in the world.

40 years later, this little secret is known, but not very widely. Our so-called modern cars are for the most part fitted with steering that does not conform to the conditions I have just described. In order to 'correct' shimmy and reactions, automobile steering has been exaggeratedly under-geared, making rapid response practically impossible. One sees in garages expensive and sophisticated machines that are difficult to drive. These cars have their wheels perfectly balanced – a useless precaution, because any form of pivot at the wheel's centre of gravity will always allow play, steering defects and imbalance, while at the same time rendering it impossible to detect the slightest problem, even with high-geared steering.

Technicians reading these lines will of course be incredulous. The proof is neither time consuming nor costly to find: a plane ticket to Majorca, an hour away, and there, any sceptical but curious technician can hire one of my 'Spanish wheelbarrows'.[7]

---

7) The Biscuter '*zapatillas*' built by Autonaçional in the fifties

The Biscooters I designed and constructed are a primitive means of transport, indifferently manufactured. But the steering axis passes through the wheel's centre of gravity, and driving a Biscooter, with its very direct steering, is a pleasure unknown to French motor enthusiasts who regard themselves as connoisseurs, whereas our vehicles are for the most part known in the trade as old nails.

In 1920, the use of rigid axles made it hard to achieve perfect steering. The modern type of 'flapping wing' suspension - an assemblage of small bits of ironmongery unworthy of an engineer - has only made things more imprecise. Like any metal under load, each component flexes to a greater or lesser degree, and these repeated flexions succeed in achieving the effect I had obtained by introducing my 'binoculars' fore and aft.

However, the modern arrangement is a morass of articulations - up to 8 per wheel, making 16 articulations for a steered front end, not counting shock absorbers and other articulated elements. This fragile and costly assembly is a dangerous imbecility because, under a strong impact, the steering loses so much of its precision that it can cause a car suddenly to roll over.

The wheel of a car rises and falls. *A single articulation* is therefore all that is necessary to assure adequate suspension, and should resolve the small problem of shock absorption, as I shall demonstrate at the end of this book.

Chapter IV

In the spring of 1922, Esmée, home alone, made me climb the seven floors to her garret. I entered a furnished attic. The woman who obsessed me shared two little rooms under the mansard roof with her mother and brother. The conveniences were at the end of a hallway. How could this pretty girl, so fresh and gay, be so well turned-out while living in this hovel with no running water?

I still owned the house in boulevard Lannes[1] that I had bought to entertain my pilot friends, and those from wartime. I installed my conquest in this little town house, and the rue Poissonnière was abandoned. In those days, there were semi-rural green spaces near the boulevard Lannes. The fortifications of Paris still stood, and on their embankments had grown meadows punctuated by spinneys. Fifteen years later, the boulevard was 'tidied up', the fortifications demolished, and the area literally choked by traffic...

Thus, I cheated on my wife. I've always disliked that expression. It contains the seeds of a kind of criminality that is one of the most damaging to our society: I think I prefer murder to cheating, the abuse of trust that dishonours men and reduces millions of defenceless beings to misery.

The state of my mother's health had worried us for a long time. The symptoms of her imminent demise made me rush to be near her. Two days after my arrival, the final moments of my dear *maman* were clearly imminent.

---

1) Acquired in 1914 from the celebrity occultist Sar Peladan

The invalid suffered constant choking fits, and it was obvious that she was going to pass away during these increasingly severe bouts. I therefore assembled all her loved ones and suggested putting an end to our martyr's sufferings by anaesthesia. My proposal was accepted without demur. I soaked a wad of cotton wool in ether and placed it over the face of my dear old *maman*. She liked the smell of ether. Her eyes opened, and I thought she threw me a glance of recognition. A few moments later, she was finally at peace. I had deliberately shortened her life. I felt not the slightest shadow of guilt when I explained what I had done to the doctor who came that afternoon, and never since has my conscience been troubled.

One of my closest friends, a practising Catholic, convinced of the existence of God, remonstrated with me one day about my private life, which he deemed to be completely beyond the pale. I then told him that my marriage had been but a civil one, and astonishingly, this reassured him of my faith. In his eyes, I was living in sin anyway, and therefore free to pursue my pleasures as I pleased!

Just as I had laid my mother to rest without remorse, I would not in fact have been able to live with myself had I been deliberately unscrupulous. I was deeply Christian, yet impure! Moreover, I was answerable to no one for matters of conscience, but an old friend, the priest of a remote parish in the Ain, took me to task one day on the subject.

"You're a fool," he says. "You believe in God as we all do, but by other names of your own choosing. In your pernickety way of thinking, God goes by the name of chance, happiness, misery, success, failure, hope, the prodigious goings-on of the world that surrounds us. Your pretentious circumlocutions would be a good deal shorter if you simply admitted the existence of God once and for all. Do you think that for me, God has the same face as that imagined by the sheep in my congregation? Come to that, why aren't you simply a Catholic?"

I listed the thousand disturbing aspects of the cult, the irrationality of its dogmas, the pomp of some of its ceremonies, the Vatican Bank.

"You'll end up by reproaching me for my cassock!" he says. "Look at me..."

Pickaxe in hands and wearing a shapeless felt hat, he was repairing the path to his chapel dressed in a torn old jumper of his housekeeper's, his cassock caked with mud and held up with coarse string, and his feet bare in broken clogs. I was tempted for a minute to remind him of the fountains of St Peter's Square in Rome, but as this highly intelligent man would have turned both barrels of his faith upon me, I refrained from any such criticism.

Unfortunately my conduct didn't improve much - at least, as far as fidelity is concerned. When I knew her, Esmée was a lead dancer in the ballet and shared a dressing room with a dozen or so future stars of the Opéra. Soon after we met, she was promoted to *petit sujet*, and *petit sujets* shared dressing rooms. This situation in itself posed little threat to my virtue, but the dressing rooms were easy to visit, and the backstage corridors of the Palais Garnier were long... In a few days of corridors, I had met the entire *corps de ballet,* which proved my undoing.

France is, it seems, populated by '*résistants*', but the word only became an *appellation controlée* after 1945. Back in 1923, we knew nothing of 'the Resistance', and I therefore knew not how to resist the allure of so many great beauties. In my defence, I could say that the ladies of the Academy of Music and Dance weren't very good at resisting, either. But I have to admit that in this monastery of grace, and therefore seduction, virtue was on the contrary quite widespread. On Judgement Day, I shall be unable to plead mitigating circumstances...

I courted the young ladies who pleased me, and my ignoble approaches were unfortunately sometimes rewarded. Esmée learned of this, and all too often I had to dry the bitter tears I caused with kisses of reassurance.

There followed a year of turpitude, crises, excuses, apologies and recidivism. My life became more and more complicated. Although I dined punctually every day in the marital home, I lunched regularly at Esmée's. But I would also take 'friends' to lunch on the same day, gulping down a delicious meal at the boulevard Lannes before rushing to a restaurant in the Bois de Boulogne to begin a second menu. When things were at their most chaotic, I would then meet a third (by then, hungry and ill-tempered) companion who awaited me at 2 o'clock. The first and second steaks were no problem, but the third was purgatory. Although overfed, I was losing weight!

One evening at the ballet, I was asked to convey a message to one of the stars of the production. Once the performance had ended, I presented myself at the dressing room of Miss Sylvia Djalini. The diamanté tutu was in the middle of the room, and Miss Sylvia was getting ready to dress for the evening. She was so scantily clad that her beauty was impossible to ignore. To complete my undoing, the mirror that covered one wall of the dressing room allowed me to admire this impressive sight from both sides. I stood paralysed with admiration at this gazelle, who embodied perfection from the roots of her hair to the tips of her high-arched feet.

As I remained silent, the star interjected "Well, why are you standing there like lemon?"

I answered as best I could, relaying the message about something or other to do with a dinner for season ticket holders.

"Are you yourself a season ticket holder?" she enquired. I had to admit to being no such thing - a freelancer, as it were. Luckily, this expression pleased the young lady, and I was invited to replace her absent dresser, a task I accomplished to the best of my ability. She proffered a hand, which with thumping heart I kissed, and left.

Overwhelmed as I was by the sight of her undressed in front of the mirror, this person was to upset my equilibrium. Breathlessly, I soon sought a rendezvous with this star I had encountered on my *via crucis*. Esmée agreed to invite Sylvia to Maxim's for lunch, and she accepted. Two days later, radiant with youth and beauty, our guest came across to where we were sitting. She took her place on the banquette next to Esmée, gulped down a jug of beer and told us she was late because some idiot had just given her a rose bush so ridiculously large that it wouldn't fit in her dressing room. Although I was of course the idiot in question, I assumed a casual air that averted my imminent humiliation.

Lunch drew to a close and Esmée left us for a rehearsal that didn't involve the star. We were alone!

"What are you going to do now?" asked my guest.

"I'm going to confess. The idiot with the rose bush was me."

"It was you who lumbered me with that tree? Be kind enough to take it away. I can't sleep in a room with flowers, and have nowhere to put your greenery at night."

I offered her a lift straight away, which she accepted. Placing the rose bush in the back seat of my torpedo, I asked Miss Djalini to come with me and help. I unloaded the bouquet at boulevard Exelmans, dug a large hole in the garden and planted the cause of my embarrassment.

That done, I invited the star to take tea. She hesitated a moment, but she was curious about my lair - and her curiosity proved my undoing. My house made a very agreeable first impression. The swimming pool, the mini-theatre, and especially the organs - because I had some of these also - surprised my beautiful visitor. Our conversation became more intimate.

"Are you the Voisin of the cars and aeroplanes?" she asked.

"I am, alas, that unworthy person. And I sense that the memory of you, if you abandon me, will turn my life upside down."

"Be careful what you say - I hear very discreditable reports of you. They say you are a Don Juan, and women find only tears, sorrow and despair in your company..."

I explained as best I could that I was not a womaniser but an industrialist, and that a car manufacturer is sometimes obliged to appear like a womaniser in order to observe certain phenomena relevant to his occupation. That, at any rate, was what I meant to have said.

"So are you courting me or not?"

"Appearances would suggest so."

"Sir, no-one has ever courted me so rudely! Let me leave at once."

Then something entirely unexpected happened. Miss Sylvia must have made a mistake, because she took three paces in the direction of my bedroom. Stupefied, I followed her with thumping heart. Her dress fell to the carpet; she was hardly dressed beneath the material which signally failed to conceal her perfection.

"Take care," she said when I approached her. "I shall yield..."

The phrase must have been some sort of spell, because it had a devastating effect on my manhood. I hoped that light-hearted chitchat would restore the faculty that had so suddenly deserted me, but it only made things worse.

"Where are you dining tonight?" she asked.

"With you. We shall drink to the rose bush, and I'll drive you back to the rue Rossini."

"Make music to me."

Defenceless, I did as she asked. In an instant, the star made me realise that I was but an insignificant amateur in so many ways. I did my best to tell her what I had to say, and this confession, punctuated by her exclamations of incredulity, laughter and sarcasm, led us to dinner. For me, the meal was both a great joy and a terrible ordeal. But when I accompanied the object of my desire home, my equipment yet again failed to rise to the occasion.

I saw Sylvia nearly every day. At around six o'clock, after a hard day at the factory, I would drive at top speed to the rue Rossini. I admired this beauty who treated me so brusquely, and I lost no time embarking on the road to conjugal bliss. Although our intimacy had made considerable progress, I remained the ridiculous personage of the semi-platonic admirer.

The August holidays took us by surprise. I left for Cannes and arranged to meet Sylvia a week later in Marseilles. I was to fetch her at Saint-Charles station by car. She was arriving from Italy, her tan making her eyes seem even larger. I suggested we visit Marseilles. At dinner, I proposed a pilgrimage to Notre-Dame-de-la-Garde.[2] Entering the basilica, I bought an impressively large votive candle, explaining to the object of my desires that this petition was my last resort.

2) The ornate neo-byzantine basilica that overlooks the old port at Marseilles.

Dinner was enchanting. My guest, in a highly romantic mood, was not only a great artist but also a very engaging companion. I was, in a word, the happiest of men, and I relied on Our Lady to rectify my hapless situation. We had never spent the night together beneath the same roof, and I secretly hoped that this would prove my salvation. But it didn't. My beautiful young companion affected impatience.

"Perhaps your candle wasn't big enough, or contaminated in some way," she said. "I'm beginning to think that you don't find me attractive; you certainly can't love me, at any rate. How I regret my indiscretion!"

I implored. I begged for patience. I wept at my own inadequacy. That night, still nothing happened. The candle had, alas, failed to move Notre-Dame-de-la-Garde...

Holding a slice of toast the next morning, I was just about to open a jar of marmalade when the miracle happened. I upset the tray and let fall the dressing gown which an instant earlier had concealed the cause of my downfall and approached the beauty who, notwithstanding the graphic evidence of my intentions, was unprepared for my advances.

Towards midday, my now sated partner wanted to go up to Notre Dame once more. I went with her. Recognising us, the sexton spoke.

"I was unable to place your candle in the chapel last night as you wished; I was only able to light it this morning, around nine o'clock!"

The candle episode didn't strike me at the time, but I thought about it later. I had experienced this phenomenon before, but in more or less understandable circumstances: I had been distracted by some insignificant detail, or a perfume to which I was allergic had wrought my undoing. In a word, I had found plausible reasons, and had I been at all worried, these would have completely reassured me. Notre-Dame-de-la-Garde had evidently got me out of trouble.

However, on taking stock I realised that since my thirtieth year my energies had waned from time to time. To my anxious eyes, my greying temples seemed a warning. At the factory, I realised a little later that although I had gained in experience, my professional faculties no longer had the aggressive character of ten years earlier.

Finally, having always had the benefit of exceptional eyesight, the 'telescope' of when I was 30 was no more. I consulted an optician, and three days later entered my office decked out in spectacles. I met Albert Descarme (*sic*) on my way. Predictably smiling, he came over and shook hands and reminded me of the old saying: 'Hello glasses; goodbye lasses'.

At 41 years old, I thought of myself as being in the prime of life but I was badly mistaken. A group of biologists was to discover 20 years later that ageing in men begins around the thirtieth year, and that the geriatric curve rises very steeply thereafter.

Whatever the outcome, love and its soaring lcaps of the heart, love's tragic surrenders, love's thunder, its crimes, twists and turns, all these joys of life were no longer mine.

"Hello glasses; goodbye lasses."

Chapter V

Things were going well at Issy-les-Moulineaux.

However, coachwork was getting heavier ever day, and the most elementary principles of aerodynamics were ignored in the name of a passing imbecility already known as '*la ligne*'. Coupés of the time flared outwards at the top like Etruscan vases, and it took week-long battles to persuade our so-called '*luxe*' clientèle to accept a rear window of acceptable dimensions.

I designed a coupé which didn't broaden out towards the roof; on the contrary, it narrowed. This arrangement gave me a reduced frontal area and allowed me to make the roof structure lighter, significantly reducing the body's centre of gravity. Colleagues immediately christened this coupé 'the Voisin coffin'. But just as truth always triumphs, these shapes that imposed themselves by brilliant rationalism were eventually adopted throughout automotive construction.

Eventually, Hispano offered potential Voisin clients a much more powerful chassis than ours, superbly designed by my friend Birkigt. Remembering the C5, our so-called sales department asked me for a dazzling demonstration of our capabilities.

These gentlemen's skills are well known: they can only sell something when buyers are already fighting each other to get hold of it. At such times, their presence serves little purpose. But when, for some economic, technical or even meteorological reason, what they have to sell no longer finds ready buyers, they're incapable of clinching a deal (or if they do,

Dominique Lamberjack and his brother Emile had were closely involved in the motor industry. Emile (who was on the board of Clément-Talbot) looked after the sales and repair of Mercedes in France in the early years. As well as being involved in the dealings around the original Artault/Dufresne/Cabaillot prototype, Dominique represented Zedel before becoming a leading agent for both Voisin and Bugatti. As can be seen overleaf, he competed in the Paris-Nice event in various Voisins over the next four years. His other long-distance driving feats include co-driving a 3½-tonne Citroën bus with 12 passengers on the 1934 Monte Carlo Rally without incurring a single penalty.

it's by such complex and costly means that it would be preferable to do nothing at all), in which case their presence is just as useless.

Once again, we were to lose precious time. I therefore prepared an 18CV chassis with an ultra-light body weighing only a few kilos, and a 150-litre fuel tank. This car was to be our last with splash lubricated bearings, and only rear wheel brakes were fitted. We deliberately adopted this outmoded specification to make the car easier for second-rate salesmen to sell.

Despite the limitations of the method of lubrication, we gave the engine some hundred or so horses. The total weight at the start line with a full tank, two spares and all tools was 1,500 kilos. The underside of the chassis was completely enclosed, and we obtained unusually aerodynamic efficiency which allowed a 150kph top speed.

Among our friends was an agent of quality, Dominique Lamberjack, a former bicycle champion who despite his poor eyesight, was an exceptional driver. On April 5th 1921, he took the road from Paris to Nice, via the Alps. Our 18CV left at around three in the morning for Fontainebleau, Saulieu, Chalon, Cuisery, Bourg, Grenoble, Digne, Puget-Théniers. Lamberjack arrived in Nice at 14:30 and 43 seconds.

This unique achievement drew unexpected publicity: dipping their pens in vitriol, local newspaper editors lambasted our firm in the harshest terms. Having identified, analysed and discussed in every conceivable literary form all the dangers of driving from Paris to Nice in eleven and a half hours, one indisputable fact remained: we had beaten the Blue Train - the fastest, most expensive and best equipped luxury train in France - by six hours.

Sporting drivers then tried to beat our exploit. But in order to do so they would have needed the skill and knowledge of the route that only Lamberjack possessed.

La 10 ch. Voisin de M. Lamberjack
dans Paris-Nice 1925
au Pesage.

PARIS-NICE
M. LAMBERJACK
SANS PENALISATION
VOISIN

PARIS-NICE
1er LAMBERJACK
SEUL SANS PÉNALISATION
VOISIN

M. Lamberjack sur 10 ch Voisin dans Paris-Nice 1925 au Col

Above: Light, functional and characteristically perpendicular: a Weymann saloon on the 8CV C4 chassis

I attempted in our publicity materials to expose the irremediable calamities that excess weight in transport could bring about. I didn't succeed, but two of my friends, Tabuteau[1] and Weymann,[2] were to clinch the argument in 1920 with their bodies of unprecedented lightness.

Like myself, Weymann and Tabuteau were mixed up in the history of aviation. They were hardened to working within the most severe constraints of which coachbuilders knew nothing. Furthermore, Tabuteau was an irrepressible 'demonstrator'.

Weymann and Tabuteau found an ingenious but robust way to stretch a 'Pégamoîd'[3] covering over an incredibly light wooden framework. Plastic products did not yet exist, and this accurate-looking imitation leather produced very agreeable results. The carefully designed doors were not as wide as the passenger compartment as is unfortunately the case in 1961, and this lightness was accompanied by a hitherto unprecedented silence.

---

1) **Maurice Tabuteau** was a record-breaking pioneer pilot, winning both the Michelin cup and the Deutsch prize. Hired by Sir George White to test the Bristol Boxkite after the Voisin-designed Zodiac biplane proved unsatisfactory, he was at Filton in 1911 while GV was working there on the all-metal Bristol monoplane he christened *Janine*. After demobilisation, he worked with Weymann on perfecting his lightweight coachwork system, the prototype of which was fitted to Tabuteau's 16CV Panhard. At the time of which GV was writing, Tabuteau was a director of the Weymann company.

2) *Sup'Aéro* graduate **Charles Weymann** knew GV at Issy when trying out the *Demoiselle* his wealthy American parents had given him for his 20th birthday. In the Farman he bought next, he attempted the first crossing of the Alps and won the Gordon Bennett International Speed Cup at Eastchurch in 1910 and 1911. Farman introduced him to Nieuport, in whose machines he won the 1913 Schneider Cup. After an irregular aerial war (as a US citizen), Weymann turned to the automobile - at first with Jaeger instruments (in which GV was a major shareholder) and Le Nivex, the pneumatic fuel gauge he initially patented for aircraft. It was when the chassis of his Rolls-Royce gave way under the weight of its formal body that he turned his attention to coachwork. The system was based on thin ash frame members joined by metal strips with a 4-6mm gap to allow flexibility. Light fabric padded with horsehair was stretched over the frame and covered with leathercloth. As well as silence and ease of maintenance, the result typically weighed less than half of a conventional equivalent. Weymann began developing the system in 1920, and it entered production early in 1923; after it fell out of fashion at the end of the decade, Weymann became involved in developing the Cotal electromagnetic gearbox.

3) Pegamoid was a US brand of Rexine-type leathercloth fabric originally developed in the 1890s for upholstery, luggage and bookbinding. By 1912, it was also marketed in the UK and France as 'aeroplane cloth' for wings and fuselages.

Modern rationalism, with no concession to fashion: a lightweight fabric-bodied factory C3 saloon of 1925

The clientèle hesitated for a year, then a few amateur competition successes triggered a stampede to our friends. By 1924, despite the multiplicity of licence holders, it was virtually impossible to get a Weymann body made within a reasonable time.

This formula should have prevailed over everything else being made in the workshops of the time, which continued denuding the forests of France. Unfortunately Weymann coachwork lacked glamour. The fabric covering couldn't match the shimmering highlights of the cellulose paint which had recently been imported from America, the country of the flashy appearances par excellence. A Weymann body, despite all Tabuteau's efforts, couldn't be 'blown over', much to the chagrin of the bodgers of Porte Maillot, used car experts convinced that the mechanical condition of a second-hand car is measured above all by the brightness of the chrome and the dazzling reflections of cheap oven-fresh paint.

Thus the magnificent Weymann bodies gradually disappeared. The attempt at this entirely original concept had nevertheless borne some fruit. Our clientèle understood that oak beams and ironmongery held together by shoddy old screws had had their day. Citroën, Renault and the Americans were by then offering their own adequately strong and often reasonably light mass-produced bodies.

Coachbuilding as it had existed up to 1920 would disappear, and a great shame it was, because these craftsmen represented an art whose perfection we can today admire only in museums. Finally, the Voisin body constructed entirely of light alloy was developing day by day, and around 1925 our chassis stopped drifting off to the workshops of Levallois, or, even more dangerously, to provincial carpentry shops.

Above: A standard four-litre C3 18CV chassis stands outside the annexe to the Issy-les-Moulineaux factory

In 1922, our agents and salesmen, our prodigious 'sales department' began calling for a less costly model. We ought to have filed away the vague demands of these gentlemen and worked without pausing for breath on our warhorse, the 18CV.

The Knight sleeve valve of our first chassis was fragile and unable to withstand the excessive loads continually imposed upon it. We had to resolve the discouragingly intractable but vital question of upper cylinder temperatures, and had already planned the programme we were going to carry out when the 10CV Panhard achieved its well-deserved success.

In the course of some tests on the possibility of gaining a few horses by lightening the connecting rods and pistons, we blew a hole in a piston. Once disassembled, I immediately set about increasing the thickness of the piston crown. We had been using magnesium in our competition engines for several months, and the density of this admirable metal permitted the considerable thicknesses required to ensure adequate heat dissipation.

Four new pistons awaited me two days later. Test bed components were made in the tool room, a workshop run by Germain, a Neuvellois, an excellent mechanic whom I had known since childhood in Neuville-sur-Saône. I then assembled the four pistons on our 18CV and the engine duly took its place on the laboratory test bench. Our most recent readings had indicated 100bhp at 2,700rpm. The engine was of course unsupercharged, but it did have twin carburettors. It was started in my presence and run in for three hours on the bench.

Our 'special' revved eagerly to 3,500rpm, then climbed to 3,900. Scarily, the test suggested nearly 150 horsepower. Certain that there must have been some mistake, I carried out six consecutive tests. Three slide rule experts were present. The result did indeed border on 150bhp at nearly 4,000rpm.

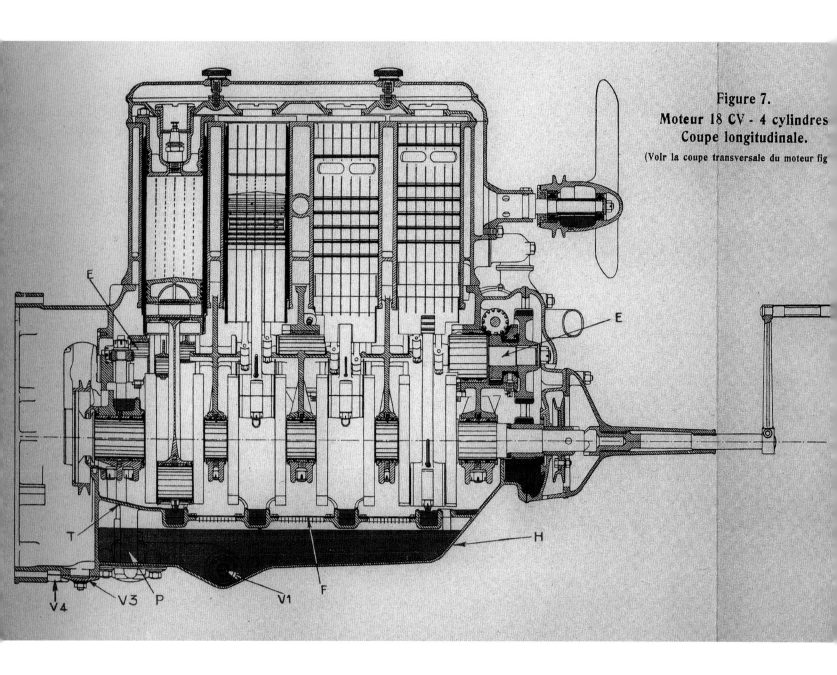

Figure 7.
Moteur 18 CV - 4 cylindres
Coupe longitudinale.

(Voir la coupe transversale du moteur fig

Whence this leap from 100 horses to 150? I had our fancifully optimistic power unit dismantled and spent the night checking it. At dawn, the reassembled engine still gave 150bhp. I then measured the fuel consumption, which turned out to be astonishing. Our combustion engine consumed 186 grammes of petrol per HP/hour, which is to say about 30 litres an hour at full power!

A second dismantling taught us nothing. I personally rechecked the dimensions of the pistons that I had sketched out for Germain five days earlier: I had made a mistake in the height, and our compression which had hitherto never exceeded 5.5:1 was now over 8.3!

At that time, 39 years ago, it was absolutely impossible to accommodate such a high compression ratio on a poppet valve engine. Surface temperatures at the inlet and exhaust - particularly the exhaust - provoked pre-ignition, which limited compression ratios. This limitation having virtually acquired the status of dogma, we had applied similar compression ratios to our sleeve valve engines without ever considering significantly exceeding these norms.

In fact, unlike the poppet valve engine, the Knight sleeve valve was by design endowed with very large inlet and exhaust ports, and although the combustion chambers were usually too hot to lubricate the mechanism adequately at full power, they were so perfectly smooth that they obviated any hot spots that would trigger premature combustion. We could therefore countenance unusually high compressions for the time, which I would not have suspected before the error which revealed this unexpected advantage. Unfortunately, as I mentioned earlier, our 18CV was fragile. The crankshaft, despite its five bearings (already!) was weak, and the main bearings were annoyingly prone to 'run'.

Above: Quintessentially Voisin, an endearingly jazzy 8CV C4 saloon.

Finally, unacceptable distortions of the entire crankcase led to inevitable failures at the power outputs our providential good fortune had revealed. To sum up, the engine would have had to undergo a major redesign in order to become a viable proposition. I began a challenging and controversial development programme, and postponed the remainder of our tests for a few weeks.

Pressed by some, harried by others, pestered by clients who thought it possible to make a cheap luxury car, I had to begin preparations for a 10CV chassis. The Salon was five months away, so there wasn't a minute to lose.

I had begun sketching with no conviction when I met a young engineer from the *Arts et Métiers*, Marius Bernard.[4] This very able technician and excellent draughtsman had been working on and had partly completed an 8CV ensemble. Marius Bernard was an infinitely appealing character in many ways. Artaud and Dufresne, for their part, whom I had literally showered with generosity, had run off to Peugeot with all our documentation. Peugeot then built a 'Voisin', but the escapade ended in failure for the famous company.[5]

---

4) Having spent the war helping to develop Panhard's 450hp V12 under Arthur Krebs, **Marius Bernard** joined Voisin at the age of 25 after a stint testing the new engine in a Voisin bomber in Voisin bombers in 1918. Thereafter, he worked with GV more or less continually from when he designed the original 8CV (later 10CV) engine until his death, while still at the helm of what remained of the Voisin factory. He left briefly in 1932, when GV sold his shares to the Belgian consortium, but remained in close contact during his brief stint at Lancia and at Weymann's Cotal works in Issy. As soon as GV returned to the factory in 1934/5, Bernard rejoined his mentor and participated on every subsequent Voisin project including the straight 12, the C30 and the C31 Biscooter.

5) The resulting 18CV Peugeot 174 was virtually a mirror-image clone of the Voisin C3, with the exhaust and inlet sides of the Knight engine reversed and left-hand steering. It was built not at Sochaux but in a small factory immediately adjacent to the Voisin works in boulevard Gambetta.

Open and closed iterations of the factory-bodied 8CV C4, finished in the voguish Caledonian style for the 1922 season

I charged Bernard with the task of sorting out all our problems, and 40 years later he left us for a better world while at the head of my old firm. By taking Bernard from me, the gods condemned to oblivion the firm that bore my name. The oldest aviation company in the world, that he single-handedly championed for too long with incredible courage, faith, diplomacy and energy, would disappear. In fact, three years after his death,[6] this company I had in part built up by my own hands went into liquidation.

Marius Bernard's design was enthusiastically adopted. Begun in July, the chassis was on test by the end of August. It was a very pretty car, in which all our observations were condensed. Presented at the Paris Salon, it met with only modest success. Our clientèle, who thought only of the Blue Train, spectacular average speeds and so-called 'luxury' appointments, was disappointed. Our 8CV, it seemed, was 'too small'.

This imbecilic argument still rages in automotive industry circles today. Buyers seem incapable of understanding that properly designed accommodation is essentially invariable, determined as it is by the human skeleton, and that when empty, long bonnets are merely a waste of space. This penchant for exterior volume is the cause of all our congestion worries and will put our industry in peril when the Common Market eliminates today's nonsensical customs duties. We shall witness the triumph of very small, perfectly comfortable cars in under the very noses of our engineers, whose self-importance and resistance to new ideas beggars belief. A glance at the little English Austin, with its small transverse engine, 450kg weight and generous interior space, should put an end to all discussion.[7]

After a brief career, the 8CV Voisin became a 10CV. This model sold relatively well, but its 100kph performance was seemingly not enough for our 'boy racers'.

6) The year after his death, in fact: 1958.

7) The kerb weight of BMC's original production ADO15 Mini was in fact 617 kg.

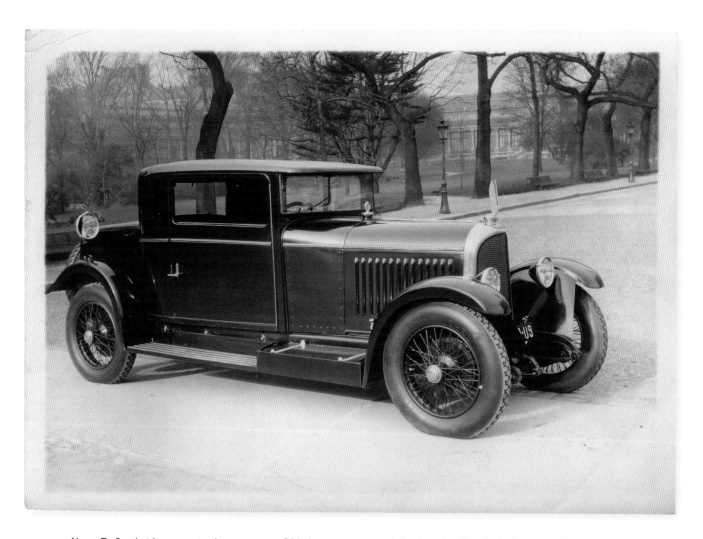

Above: Defiantly idiosyncratic, this prototype C11 three-seater coupé (body code: Chambellan) is an early example of Marius Bernard's small six. Although referred to throughout as the 13CV, the C11 first had a 14CV rating. The model was reclassified as a 13CV by the *Service des Mines* in 1928, and called the C14. Both are virtually identical in specification.

I rolled up my sleeves, Bernard faithfully followed suit and the 4-cylinder 10CV grew into a 13CV 6-cylinder, a car that was to be one of our greatest successes.

My adventures at the Opéra, my complicated personal life, my woes at the factory with much time lost on often futile tests, and finally the tedious round of regional competitions, had taken up unimaginable amounts of time. I lived in the most dreadful disorder. My boat *Ariel* still awaited me at Meulan. It was comfortably equipped, and I could receive friends there. Aft, there was a crew station for two, a galley and a lounge/dining room containing concealed couchettes. In the front, a very comfortable bedroom, a bathroom, and, off a central alleyway, two perfectly fitted cabins had transformed the former warship into a very agreeable (if not particularly elegant) motor yacht. All that was lacking was time, and that I could not find.

I had planned a securely braced mast for my vessel, as I wanted to use it as a derrick - and to cap it all, *Ariel* had square-rigged sails. Everything was varnished, painted, repainted, well maintained and ready for a big voyage. We were going to sail up the Seine and the Yonne and then to use the Canal de Bourgogne at Laroche-Migennes to gain access to the Saône. Having sailed down the Saône, we would follow the Rhône until Saint-Louis-de-Rhône, and from there, crossing the Golfe de Fos in the Mediterranean, head for Cannes. In all, nearly 1800 kilometres of navigation. The voyage took five weeks.

Chapter VI

In my absence, the bureaucratic party seized power...

The power in question was to circumscribe Marius Bernard and to 'direct' him in our new design, the 13CV 6-cylinder. A sort of steamroller, complete with harmonious curves, had already taken shape, luckily on paper only. I had to get rid of these imbeciles, whom I never saw again. In my company, every interference with the technical division by the so-called sales department ended in disaster, both financially and mechanically. That is not to say that motor industry sales departments should not be consulted by engineers, but that these consultations must be limited to requests and suggestions that must be edited with great precision. In my view, a sales department must never intervene technically in even the smallest details of a design.

Bernard was devastated. Only recently admitted into the inner circle, the importance he had gained in a very short time had provoked adverse reactions amongst the far too numerous panjandrums of our sales department, which in turn had made him cautious. He waited for my presence to reassert itself, after which we would together undertake a rich and fruitful body of work.

Before sketching out anything, we had to deal with three questions of the utmost importance. Our Knight sleeve valve engines suffered from three unacceptable vices: firstly, the fragility of the sleeves; secondly, the weakness of the bearings; thirdly, the BOUM.

Engines operated by single or double sleeves are costly to make but their advantages are indisputable. Pre-eminent among these virtues is that sliding sleeves allow incomparably larger inlet and exhaust ports than any poppet valve mechanism. The second is absolutely precise distribution, irrespective of engine speed, because both inlet and exhaust ports are opened and closed desmodromically. The third virtue is silence: valveless distribution is inaudible. Some of our cars have now been in use for 30 years, and their distribution remains as it was on the day they were first delivered.

For so many advantages not to have been more widely adopted, sleeve valve distribution therefore has to have a fatal flaw: fragility.

Driving flat out in the way that poppet valve engines can more or less withstand is FATAL to sleeve valve engines. In effect, distribution in a sleeve valve takes place in the heat of the explosion itself, and extreme upper cylinder temperatures can 'cook' the film of oil which the sliding of the surfaces depends. Under the action of the intense heat of combustion, lubricating oil is distilled, which produces tars and carbon deposits; the sleeves seize, stuck to one another or against the cylinder block, and an accident becomes inevitable - expensively so, because breakage is the usual result of sticking sleeves.

During the initial trials of the 10CV, we established that a reduction in bore improved heat transfer, and for this reason was less demanding in terms of lubrication. We therefore opted for a 75mm bore with the 13CV. One of our 10CVs under test at prolonged high engine speeds revealed the inexplicable appearance of gas bubbles in the water tank. I had a junk head made whose upper part was open to the elements so as to be able to observe this phenomenon, and Bernard, who was overseeing the tests, came to fetch me one morning to show me something incredible.

Our junk heads, covered by 30cms of water, glowed red before our eyes. The effects of heat took their course and bubbles of gas rose to the surface of the liquid.

We were dumbstruck. Our junk heads were of steel, and their base, in contact with water at 45 degrees, was 7mm thick where they were reddening. I decided to cut the junk heads open and to pour in some pewter which, once adhered to the steel, increased the thickness so as to facilitate thermal transfer through the walls

An hour later, we were ready for another test, and before our very eyes the pewter in contact with the coolant melted and deformed, creating cavities and peaks. The thickness of the base of each head was then increased from 7mm to 10, then 12mm. It no longer glowed red.

How had our 18CV, with a bore of 95mm, been able so valiantly to resist such a dangerous phenomenon?

The answer is simple: our four-litre engine put around 100 horses at our clients' disposal, and on the road it was impossible to make use of all 100 for the time needed to increase the temperatures to this point. The 13CV we were planning to build was far more vulnerable than the four-litre in this respect.

Our guinea pig rapidly became a forest of thermometers, and the junk heads took the form they should have done in the first place - with substantial 'buttresses' connecting the centre that carried the spark plug to the wall abutting the inner sleeve - and our engine at last became satisfactorily robust.

The conventional four stroke engine, which provides useful energy only once every two revolutions, is doomed. For all its many elegant executions, this engine will be replaced by two-strokes, which are far more economical to make. Two-strokes can be subdivided into two categories:

1. The least expensive of all engines, whose distribution is achieved solely by apertures in the cylinder.

2. A much more expensive solution with far higher thermal output. This involves a method of distribution which can only be fully realised by means of one or two sleeves. In this case, the sleeves, the heads, and all parts of the engine subjected to combustion temperatures must be designed with infinite care in order to operate for an hour at full power at bearing surface temperatures not exceeding 120 degrees, without which conditions the engine is consigned to certain failure irrespective of the most optimistic interventions to the contrary.

The second weakness of our engines concerned the bearings. Our new designs involved far higher engine speeds and mean pressures, since I fully intended to adopt higher compression ratios in view of what our tests with the 18CV had revealed.

At that time - and incredibly, still now - an engine's connecting rods and bearings relied on white metal; astonishingly, this was and continues to be systematically replaced by ball or roller bearings anywhere aft of the rearmost engine bearing.

White metal is an amalgam of soft metals related to lead. Thus this alloy, applied in the form of 'shells' has similar frictional characteristics to conventional 'ferrodo' (*sic*), with the difference that 'ferrodo' easily withstands high temperatures whereas white metal instantly melts at the slightest provocation.

Why were our bearings not as robust as the rest of our artefacts? The problem was difficult to resolve, and, without discouraging ourselves, we tackled it by the statigraphic method so dear to Egyptologists.

Our first test was carried out thus: with one piston of our test rig at top dead centre, I replaced the spark plug of the cylinder in question by an attachment connected to a pump for testing steam boilers. This pump was equipped with a manometer for measuring pressure.

The bore of our test rig was 75mm. I pumped enough fluid into the combustion chamber to obtain a pressure of 30cms per square kilo. The 75mm bore generated about 1300 kilos of load on the bearing, that is to say the pressure applied to the piston, bearing and crankshaft journal at the instant of combustion.

We were using a crankcase cut open to allow easy observation. Now imagine our surprise on noticing that under this 1300-kilo pressure, the con rod seized on the crank pin and the crankshaft in turn seized in its bearings, preventing any further movement.

Supposing that a foreign body was obstructing the rotation of our test rig, I reduced the pressure in the combustion chamber and the mechanism ran freely. On pumping the pressure up again, it immobilised itself. Bernard pointed out that the ensemble was clearly seizing because the circulation of lubricating oil was not providing the necessary counter-pressure.

I installed a secondary pump and renewed the experiment. The test rig still did not turn.

I increased the oil pressure to 50 kilos, and the test rig remained immobile. Therefore (and the experiment can be verified today), the mechanical efficiency of white metal is so weak that an engine thus equipped can be 'statically' immobilised by applying a pressure equal to combustion pressure to its moving parts.

The old saws about 'spider's web' channels engraved into bearings and the tricks of canny fettlers having yielded no result, I had the idea to mill a groove ON THE CRANK PIN - a groove which passed by the oil feed aperture, cut at a steep angle in the direction of rotation and sloping away in the opposite direction. It then proved possible to start our test rig with 12 or 15 kilos per square centimetre on the piston at TDC.

The situation improved. Conclusions were easy enough to draw: the 1300-kilo pressure on the bearing had pressed it so hard against the oilway feeding the crankshaft that no lubricant was able to pass and as the oil film was displaced by the pressure, the ensemble seized up.

It then occurred to me to drill two 2mm holes near each face of the bearing, corresponding to each end of the groove in the crank pin. In this way, the oil on the bearing was renewed with every rotation, cooling the white metal without compromising oil pressure. These two holes had another advantage: they allowed the expulsion of impurities that otherwise would have remained trapped in the bearing.

I had an engine built with this arrangement. Although admittedly under light load, it ran for a week at 4,000rpm, which at the time was considered recklessly imprudent, and the oil temperature reduced by 26 degrees. It was a success.

The four-litre - here, a long wheelbase C3L - was the model most often bodied by third party coachbuilders.

The third vice of our engines was the 'boom', whose causes and remedy turned my hair white five years prematurely.

Here is what the 'boom' consisted of: with the car was running at low rpm in top gear, the driver, wanting to accelerate without changing down (because for years drivers ignored gearchanges and persisted in climbing the steepest gradients on the accelerator alone), would press the pedal and the engine would cease its pleasingly regular rhythm. In its place, from the very bowels of the machine, would appear an indefinable but thoroughly disagreeable muffled noise every two revolutions. Our testers called this sound of distant thunder the 'boom'.[1]

It goes without saying that the potential Voisin buyer was immediately warned of this by salesmen for rival firms, so that the 'boom' became our competitors' secret weapon. When asked, my testers blamed excessive play, without specifying where or of what type.

Tolerances were checked, but the 'boom' persisted. We then considered the ignition system. Though we had recently switched to Delco coil ignition, our mechanics preferred the outdated and temperamental magneto to this near-perfect device. A magneto therefore replaced the distributor on one of our chassis, but the 'boom' remained.

However, one of the factory hacks we had equipped with a distributor for testing purposes had a far less obtrusive 'boom'. I had the car stripped down and noticed that one of the distributor pawls had appreciably retarded the timing. Retarding the ignition of one of the production chassis by the same amount, I discovered that the 'boom' was greatly diminished.

---

1) *The Autocar* remarked on this uncharacteristically intrusive rumble from the engine when accelerating sharply from low speeds in their first test of the 4-litre in 1920.

I conjectured that the position of the pistons might somehow be drifting out of true, so the crankshafts were all meticulously checked and dynamically balanced. The first thing to determine was where the 'boom' originated - was it affecting the first, second, third or fourth cylinder?

To clarify this, I constructed a sort of ancillary combustion chamber that could be screwed into the spark plug aperture, and to which the plug of the cylinder to be checked could be fitted. It could of course be mounted on any cylinder. I used this apparatus to modify the ignition site and lower the compression ratio in the cylinder concerned.

My device succeeded perfectly. The 'boom' only occurred on number four cylinder, at the moment when the inlet cycle and the resistance to rotation were at their maximum, and ignition took place. But we still didn't know why.

I lived and breathed 'boom', the technical department ate and drank 'boom', and pretty soon clients who had never heard the 'boom' discovered this mysterious noise thanks to some indiscretion or other, which involved me in voluminous correspondence.

One day I had the preposterous notion of measuring the torsional strength of our crankshafts under the considerable pressure of each explosion. The test was simple. I immobilised a crankshaft on our engine stand by means of a bar across the flywheel, the crankshaft at 20 degrees before top dead centre, and pumped 30 kilos of pressure in the first cylinder. The journal duly descended before my horrified eyes - under the pressure of combustion, our crankshaft twisted by no less than six degrees along its length!

The explanation of the 'boom' was simple: the leading cylinders were firing on what was in effect a spring. With the last cylinder winding up the car's braking couple in this way, the boom was produced by the fact that the consequent loads at the front were much greater than those at the rear. I hadn't found an inexpensive remedy, but at least I understood the problem.

After pondering the question for a couple of days, I remembered that the valve timing on our competition engines differed from our touring cars, being heavily advanced so as to maximise induction at high engine speeds. This of course compromised the induction efficiency of our racers at low revs, but this trait is of no consequence in the hands of a professional racing driver. I then wanted to try this degree of advance on one of our production engines, on cylinder number four alone. In other words, I hoped to achieve only partial induction on this cylinder at low engine speeds to diminish the pressure of the explosion.[2]

One Sunday, accompanied by Lefebvre and Bernard, I took out on test a production chassis into which we had substituted competition sleeves on the fourth cylinder. The 'boom' was no more! We put the chassis back with no further alterations, and the next morning Bernard circulated an anodyne little note announcing this modification along with three or four other trifling matters.

When I arrived at the factory on Monday morning, Mazoyer was waiting for me on the boulevard Gambetta by the chassis with the modified engine. Smirking cryptically as he took the wheel, my expert asked me to accompany him on a test run.

"Listen to the 'boom'," he said. I assumed an innocent air. Mazoyer beamed. Without telling me, he had ordered an adjustment to the steering the previous week, and coincidentally, this had been carried out the very same chassis on which we had changed the two sleeves.

---

2) Napier had adopted a similar solution to this unpleasant roughness when pulling hard from very low revs by having a concave crown for the rearmost piston of its six-cylinder 40/50 Type 75 in 1919. In Acton's case, the thump from the rear main bearing was said to have been accentuated by localised 'diaphragming' of the crankcase.

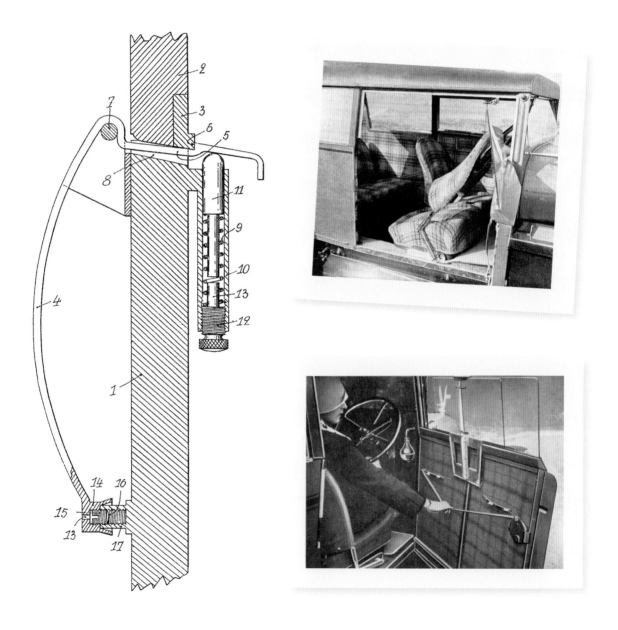

Admiringly, I congratulated him. The modification of the inlet arrangements was noticed by no one, but the steering adjustment was religiously conserved. The big obstacle had been overcome. All that remained was a series of drawings, meticulous attention to detail and a concerted effort to eliminate any remaining surplus weight, perfect the lubrication system and deal all the other details that make up an automobile whose construction has been designed with rigour.

The 2.1 litre 13CV chassis weighed 700 kilos. Using only aluminium, we found it easy to body it luxuriously for no more than 300 kilos. Eventually, we put on the market a very aerodynamic one tonne motorcar producing 70bhp at 3,200rpm.[3]

That was the moment when I envisaged door closing by a 'croissant' device.[4] I'm very proud of this method, now universally adopted, but the plagiarists have been careless enough to retain only its external form. They wilfully complicate the self-evident simplicity and total safety of what I had conceived.

The doors of most cars remain dangerous, and anyone with the misfortune to plunge off a bridge into the waters of a shallow canal below is likely to perish by drowning without being able to open their coffin.

Our 13CV was launched with a three-speed gearbox. Used without due care, our engines revved too highly, and I feared problems. The Cotal electromagnetic gearbox had just appeared at that time, and I was using its planetary gear system to fit an electric overdrive operated from below the steering wheel to the drive shaft behind the three-speed gearbox.

3) In fact, C11 and C14 models had 2.3 litre engines, and the chassis weighed around 920 kg. The engine developed 60bhp at 4000rpm (the guaranteed rev limit), and 66bhp for those brave enough to venture to 4400rpm.

4) See patent 582.766, applied for in June 1924 (two years before the 6-cylinder 13CV was introduced).

Cie Intle Voisin HR. 2 Portes. Glaces basculantes sur 14 Ch. Code Chartcorum

This innovation met with unprecedented success. Fully laden, our 13CV achieved nearly 125kph at 3,000rpm. In effect, it had the benefit of six speeds, two of which were engaged separately by switch. This device was adopted by several of the more farsighted manufacturers, and should be developed for the small cars that will soon sweep away the old-fashioned confections of today.

I needed to be careful about how these events had changed my personality into something which didn't come naturally. I had to be simultaneously aloof yet familiar, fastidious yet accommodating, demanding, precise, reserved, caring and, in order to fulfil the role of a respected industrialist, I would often exaggerate the strengths or weaknesses of my disguise.

The technical resources of our experimental department were skeletal: eight or ten young people worked with Bernard and Lefebvre, and every single day they gave me of their best. The announcement of a new project would provoke incredible competitiveness in this team, which was both a constant pleasure and a danger which had to be diplomatically contained because a (usually excellent) design can't be rejected out of hand simply because it doesn't fit current plans.

A true engineer, talented and creative, capable of expressing his ideas through his own draughtsmanship, is constantly in danger of being distracted by the seductions of some ingenious little contrivance or other. The role of technical overseer then becomes difficult. With infinite precaution, the exercise can only be redirected to its well-defined goal by expressions of apparent interest, kindly observations and gradual nudges back towards the true objective.

I introduced another method. After examining a proposition that often contained excellent intentions, I gave a young man absolute freedom of action. He would then throw himself frenziedly into refining the design, embarking on the details of ruinously costly mechanisms of dubious utility, until eventually one fine morning I would see all the tracings neatly stuffed into the waste paper basket.

I know little of current methods, but I adopted right from the earliest days a procedure that has always helped me. It consists of defining the dimensions of the main components as accurately as possible and then, on a very small scale so as to apprehend the ensemble as a whole, determining the different aspects of my design in profile, plan, elevation and so on. On completing these small scribbles, I begin enlarging, always to fixed scale: for a car of between two and six seats, I go up to a scale of 1:5, or 20 centimetres per metre. Any construction whatever must be homogeneous, and only the process of rendering the totality in small scale can instantly inform the engineer of common mistakes - the errors of trying to tie down an elephant with string.

Only then do I redraw all the individual components, and having done so, I build the definitive model (still at $1/5^{th}$ scale), which lacks only minor details: the controls, transmission components, conduits and so on. On a very large drawing table, taking my 1:5 model as reference, I then do the life-size drawing down to the smallest detail, from which the technical department subsequently extracts all the information they require.

I allow myself to remind the legions of over-simplifiers (unfortunately increasingly common) that a battleship or cargo vessel of 60,000 tonnes is drawn life size... This practice, I hasten to add, is incompatible with vertical drawing boards, which I blame in part for today's technical weakness and the timidity of our current creations.

A draughtsman should be able to apply his entire being to careful reflection, and this can only take place in the absence of all unnecessary physical effort. A designer can only work seated. He must have to hand a compass, a ruler, set square and most of all, an eraser. The fact is, small vertical drawing boards are used to cram in as many staff as possible into a given space, and result in innumerable inconveniences that are completely inimical to inspiration.

Around 1925, when it was time for the Voisin company to offer a new model, allocating the design studies was problematic. Of my 12 loyalists, four were eager to design the engine, three self-effacingly volunteered to do the gearbox and clutch, but I only found two who were inspired by the suspension and rear axle. I knew very well that the chassis, brakes, controls, steering and especially the so-called 'secondary' details in which reside the pleasure of a well-designed car, would be reserved for myself.

Chapter VII

I would have profited from putting my personal life on the test bench, which would have taught me valuable lessons...

The infernal divinities had alas decided on my damnation, and I was under rigorous surveillance. The labyrinth of complications in which I lived held out little hope, and the passage of time had brought me neither philosophy nor wisdom. Serenity seemed so remote that I had lost all hope of achieving it by the time it was eventually granted me in the twilight of my days. I was weak, and while not being a complete womaniser, I knew not how to resist the traps that continually reappeared before me.

Precisely at the time I was drawing the final components of the 13CV, I spotted a stunning young woman one evening amongst the *quadrilles*. Though her terpsichorean talents were modest, her sheer beauty made her shine like a star of the first rank. I learned a few days later that this *quadrille* measured 52cm around the waist and 90cm around the hips. Feminine beauty in those days was not yet quantified by breast measurements, and the young lady's corsage contained hardly twice the hollowed palm of an honest man's hand. This divine being was unfortunately afflicted with an over-anxious mother who would not let her little girl out of her sight for a moment.

The dancer Peretti,[1] every one of whose ballets Paris applauded, was one day kind enough to give me some old but nonetheless true advice. The fact that this was a young man who could roll the 'r's in 'six shillings of sausages' made his proposition sound irresistible:

---

1) At this time (1927), **Serge Peretti** had just been named *premier danseur* at the Opéra. 10 years earlier, aged only 12, he had made his way from Milan to the Paris Opéra; his work with Serge Lifar in the 30s drew great acclaim.

"Trrry charrrming herrr motherrr"

The siege of this very respectable lady was neither long nor arduous. In exchange for certain favours I was admitted to the company of the young artist. I was becoming cynical, and this cynicism was to hasten my undoing.

I did everything to please. I wasn't fat; rather scrawny, in fact. I had all my hair, but it was greying. Despite my assiduous attentions, despite the favours which I happily conceded, my overtures were getting nowhere. My attentiveness had been exemplary, so I was at a loss.

Every evening of the ballet, I would drive this beauty and her mother to the theatre. Then, parked in the complicitous shadows of the rue d'Antin and still with the chaperone, I would await the moment when the young girl would appear running towards us. I would take my guests immediately to a discreet cabaret and then drive them home.

I awaited the object of my concupiscence (well-concealed as usual) one evening. Madame Mother sat in the back seat of my saloon. All Voisins were right hand drive, and as I was parked on the right hand kerb, the front passenger seat was therefore on the street side. I saw my beautiful passenger arrive. I opened the door for her, to be assailed by Chanel No.5. I was just about to drive off when a woman I hadn't noticed opened the door I had just closed, and glanced into the car. It was Esmée.

Someone must have warned her of my presence in the rue d'Antin, and my *petit sujet* must have been following my *quadrille*. I was horribly embarrassed. Shaking, Esmée struggled vainly to find words with which to condemn my culpable conduct. Eventually, between sobs, she pointed her index finger at the young woman and said something to the effect that:

"I knew it would be her and her pimp of a mother!"

An appalling silence followed this outburst. The door slammed like a pistol shot as I drove off. Tight lipped, Madame Mother frostily congratulated me on the manners of my friends. We were at war.

I saw Esmée neither that evening nor the next. The situation was worsening. I was seeking ways to engineer a rapprochement when I learned by chance of a small farm for sale on the banks of the Saône near Mâcon, at Saint-Martin-Belle-Roche. A friend in Lyon was prepared to buy the cottage in Esmée's name.

Peace was signed that same day, and we spent the next week together at Saint-Martin-Belle-Roche. Esmée had never lived in the country; for her, *L'Angelo* was a revelation. An easily accepted resignation relieved my farm girl of her obligations at the Opéra, and the time I spent in the company of this laughing young woman, brimming with projects, flowed uninterrupted by anything but happy memories.

Esmée's departure from the Palais Garnier allowed me more assiduously to court Sylvia, whose career was becoming firmly established. The house in rue Rossini was abandoned. The young star also lived at the boulevard Lannes. Her life was to become that brilliant existence, permanently surrounded by admirers, that a beautiful woman and celebrated artist can expect from Paris.

Sylvia, whose life I shared very often, never presented me to her circle in the world of the arts and the theatre. The reputation I had acquired probably worried her, and I played the role in her life of a somewhat secret vice. Sylvia's circumstances tied her to the Opéra. Sometimes I could whisk her off at midnight to take her for an extravagant trip for a day or two. I would drive my beautiful captive South, towards the light and the sun...

Then things turned sour. Sylvia was about to reach heights that were inaccessible to me. We were still together, but a shadow grew between us that I was unable to dispel. It was Sylvia who one day much later confided to me the reason:

"It wasn't at the time we first met that the difference in our ages was a problem; it's now, when you reached life's irreversible turning point, while I am still capable of loving you as I did on the very first day..."

I searched in vain for a reply to this fact, so clearly expressed. I was free, my daughter was married, and we could perhaps have some happiness together for what remained of my life. But after? I knew all the dangers of an uncertain future. Horrid, detestable, cruel old age had dried up my heart...

In 1925, Issy-les-Moulineaux was at the height of its success. In four years of ceaseless endeavour and constant battling, we had secured a virtually unique position in the French motor industry.

Compared to those of Louis Renault or André Citroën, our resources were derisory. My inclination towards continual research had led me to neglect a number of industrial projects I had entrusted to inexpert hands. Endless modifications disrupted the continuity and rhythm of production and we slid slowly but surely towards a kind of poorly organised cottage industry. This state of affairs could only increase the price of our products, and to justify those prices we had constantly to put our company at the forefront of the many competitions that took place not only in France but elsewhere in Europe since, paradoxical as it may seem, we did export.

Eklund sur Voisin sport gagne la Coupe de l'A.C.R. de Suède (Février 1922)

From 1920 to 1925, we carried off 94 first prizes in these increasingly demanding contests. The factory's store rooms were cluttered with tinware including 59 trophies, and the big records in the touring car category were ours. These weren't world records, but official times at hillclimbs and speed trials here, there and everywhere.

Our 153 victories constituted a first rate sales proposition, but I was constantly preparing special machines to maintain the momentum of this programme, consuming all my ingenuity and creative faculties in the process. Our tooling was primitive, its output miserable, and more seriously, its accuracy was declining.

It was a mess that had to be rectified. I cancelled the less important events in our racing calendar and decided to take part only in major international competitions organised by The Automobile Club de France, the Royal Automobile Club of Sweden, the Royal Automobile Club Gold Shield and Shaw section and other similar bodies. In most of these grands prix, there were categories included to make up the numbers: the first of the greens, yellows or blues would win their little title and publicise it to their advantage. But our clientèle questioned these subclassifications and valued only 'First place, all categories'.

The winner of these races was of course the fastest, best braked, best balanced and strongest. The clubs, however, complicated matters by introducing limits on fuel consumption and coachwork dimensions.

In 1922, the Automobile Club de France instituted the *Grand Prix de Tourisme*, to be run for 700 kilometres on quite a challenging course in Strasbourg. The regulations imposed a minimum body width of 1.3m at the height of the front seats, and a maximum fuel and oil consumption of 16 litres per 100 kilometres. There were no weight restrictions.

Though numerous, the other contenders posed us no threat. Only Peugeot, who as we have seen, had welcomed the two traitors Artault and Dufresne the year before, along with all our documentation. With considerably greater resources than us, Peugeot presented what were in effect Voisins by another name at the 1922 Strasbourg *Grand Prix de Tourisme*. Unfortunately for them, a year had passed between the departure of the two plagiarists from Issy-les-Moulineaux and our encounter in Strasbourg - a year we had put to good use by working our hearts out.

There could be no question of entering our new 13CV of only 2.5 litres[2] for the Grand Prix, so I concentrated all my efforts on our 18CV warhorse. We had extracted 150bhp at 4,000rpm from this engine, but I was certain that this output could not be reliably sustained under these conditions for 700 kilometres. Our first concern was to strengthen the crankcase by means of transverse steel braces to increase its rigidity - a measure that succeeded perfectly in eliminating longitudinal and transverse flex. I retained the 8:1 compression ratio, but I fitted the engines (we had entered three cars) with small carburettors which, wide open and under full load, allowed only 120bhp at 3,600rpm.

Goudard and Menesson[3] from the Solex company, the prodigious engineers who were later to design and manufacture the marvellous Vélosolex, took the carburetion in hand, and our flat-out trials yielded a fuel consumption unheard of in modern engines: 182 grammes per bhp/hour. The reasons for this prodigious diesel-like frugality only became apparent to me much later on, and I set them out here for consideration by our young engineers.

---

2) Both the small six-cylinder models in fact had 2.3 litre engines.

3) **Maurice Goudard** and **Marcel Mennesson** first set up shop while still at the École Centrale in 1905, producing centrifugal drum radiators for Schneider buses. Their surnames being too long to fit on a small header tank, they held a competition to find a short, internationally pronounceable name: hence Solex. The Vélosolex that became so ubiquitous in post-war France originated from the period when GV was working on the Voisin *Motor Fly* motorised bicycle.

In the first place, the Knight sleeve valve was an engine whose inlet and exhaust ports had a surface area as large as the cylinder bore. These apertures, of a size unheard of in any other form of distribution, were obtained by the two sleeves moving in opposite directions at a stroke of 40mm.

This is not to say that a Knight engine could be envisaged today; such a fantasy would mean spending ridiculous amounts of time and money to arrive at a commercially viable end product.

At our disposal therefore, are two very large ports allowing unusually generous induction and exhaust. Secondly, distribution by sleeves is extremely mechanically efficient. In a Knight engine, the inner sleeve descends at the same time as the piston on the firing stroke, considerably enhancing mechanical efficiency. Finally, as I mentioned earlier, our crankshaft was at its torsional limit. Being very small in diameter, the rotation of the crank pins and journals absorbed little energy.

Braced with internal struts, the crankcase now remained very rigid, allowing perfectly desmodromic inlet and exhaust distribution. In combination, these factors gave us an engine whose mechanical efficiency was far greater than was usual at the time. The 8:1 compression ratio, exceptionally high for 1922, yielded unexpected thermal advantages. At one stage we feared spark plug problems; small diameter plugs didn't yet exist, but the enormous suction of our unheated induction, which verged on freezing point even in midsummer, gave us what we hoped for: admirably cooled upper cylinders.

The bodywork stipulated by the ACF's sporting committee imposed considerable width, but as the regulations only mentioned an external jig, I designed a body (in aluminium of course) 0.90m wide. To bring it up to the required 1.3m, I incorporated a tapering

148

longitudinal bulge protruding 20cms from each side panel. Though well within the regulations, my solution allowed me to create a far more aerodynamic form than the useless bodies carted around by our competitors.

Our car weighed 1,134 kilos ready to go. With 120bhp powering an aerodynamic package, we were full of optimism at the start. I had entered three cars. The names of the three drivers escape me now, but we probably chose Rougier[4], Duray[5] and Gaudermen.[6]

In those days, the Grand Prix of the ACF was commercially very important. Our drivers were constantly being solicited by various suppliers to endorse everything from tyres and batteries to fuel gauges and other impedimenta. I had to outflank these beggars, who of course offered our men substantial sums for choosing some accessory or other, and these manoeuvres were a constant source of conflict.

On the day of the race, our three cars were identical. We were to cover the 700 kilometres of the race at an average of 107kph, and our results were all that we hoped for: our competitors were annihilated.

---

4) After an illustrious career as a works driver for Turcat-Méry and De Dietrich since the 1903 Paris-Madrid, the Marseillais former cyclist **Henri Rougier** accrued further fame and wealth as an early customer of *Les Frères Voisin*, winning the Grand Prix de Berlin in 1909 and being the first to fly across the Mediterranean (in 1911, when he also drove a Turcat-Méry to victory in the inaugural Monte Carlo rally). After the war, he became one of the Paris concessionaires for Voisin and Steyr alongside several other motoring accessory interests.

5) Having secured the world land speed record (at 134.76kph) in a Gobron Brillié in 1903 and successfully campaigned De Dietrichs in the great Edwardian races on both sides of the Atlantic, the US-born Belgian **Arthur Duray** flew both Voisin and Farman biplanes in competition and won further fame by bringing the twin cam GP Peugeot to 2nd place in the Indianapolis 500 in 1914 (when he narrowly failed to take the LSR once again in the 28-litre Fiat S76).

6) **Richard Gaudermann** had driven for Voisin several times in the summer of the previous year, winning the tourism category in the Boulogne meeting and the hillclimbs at Vimille and Planfoy. An ex-footballer, he had started out as a works driver for Clément Bayard in the 1907 Targa Florio and narrowly escaped death later that year when, as riding mechanic, he was involved in Albert Clément's fatal accident during practice for the 1907 Grand Prix. He drove for Motobloc in the Coppa Florio and the Grand Prix de l'ACF at Dieppe the following year.

arrivée de Gaudermen sur 8 ex Voisin, au circuit des Routes Pavées - Septbre 23.
1er du classement général, toutes catégories.

The three first places were ours. As for fuel consumption, we had enough of the allocated 16 litres per 100 kilometres left at the end to wash down all the other contenders' cars...

The silver trophy of the *Grand Prix de l'Automobile Club de France* remains in pride of place in my private collection, and my heart still races every time I see it.

In 1923 a small contest called the *Circuit des Routes Pavées*[7] was held in the North of France. My old friend Charles Faroux[8] was one of the organisers, such a talented man that I could not refuse to enter our marque. I entered an ultra-lightweight 10CV, which came first in all categories.[9]

Spectacular as this victory was, it had been very hard fought. The appalling roads of the circuit had destroyed the most of our competitors' cars during the race. The winning 10CV was put away in a hangar of the factory annexe and forgotten until an accident reminded us of its existence.

7) The 'Circuit of cobbled roads' was in fact first held on September 29th 1922, when it was won by André Lagache in a 3-litre Chenard-Walcker at an average speed of 42mph; second was Maurice Becquet in an 18CV Peugeot (the four-litre Voisin clone); Lamberjack brought the 1.5 litre Voisin in third place ahead of the two remaining Peugeots, which claimed the team prize. The 13-kilometre course at Pont-à-Marcq on the outskirts of Lille was exceptionally hard on the cars; at one point, there was a 10-inch ridge of *pavé* across the road, banked with dirt, which threw the cars into the air in order to test their suspension. The race was last held in 1931.

8) **Charles Faroux** (1872-1957) was the doyen of French motoring commentators during the inter-war years. As editor of *La Vie Automobile*, he wrote with consistent admiration of GV and his products. As a driver, he had raced a Motobloc against Gaudermann and Duray in the 1908 Coppa Florio; as well as being co-instigator of the Le Mans 24 Hours he served as race director from 1923 to 1956. It was also Faroux who first proposed that Grand Prix grid order should be decided by practice times (at Monaco in 1933).

9) Gaudermann's Voisin in fact came third; Maurice Rost drove a 2-litre Georges Irat to victory in 1923, with Foresti's Aries in second place.

I was at the Gaumont cinema one night watching an enchanting Douglas Fairbanks film. Halfway through, a loudspeaker gurgled and we heard an announcement asking Mr Voisin to go to the manager's office. I duly left my seat and headed for the entrance, where I was met by Louis Gaumont, who came to inform me that a fire had broken out in the factory annexe.

I arrived at Issy-les-Moulineaux a little later to see that the fire had destroyed some of our stock. The material losses weren't irremediable, but that part of the factory contained completed cars ready for delivery. We were to face serious difficulties with our 'insurers' and clients alike.

Two young crooks employed in my factory had organised a remarkable swindle. With the aid of another rogue, they had contrived an entire 'insurance' whose name escapes me now. We paid premiums to this little gang, but the day of the disaster, the swindlers suddenly became impossible to find. An action was brought and a derisory penalty imposed a year later, and our trusting naïvety was exposed for all to see. At the time, we were already being affected by the upheavals of 1929, although we couldn't foresee the extent or duration of the Great Depression.

The affair of the fire was more or less over when I remembered our 10CV of the *Routes Pavées*. The car had not been destroyed in the sheltered corner it had occupied when the fire broke out - yet it had disappeared. Albert Decarme conducted an inquiry and made a distressing discovery: three of my legal 'experts' had sneaked the car away and sold it to Renault for the ridiculous sum of nearly 100,000 1925 francs.

I was a friend of Louis Renault, and I went to see him the day after my discovery to demand an explanation. Although visibly unaware of this singular transaction, he assured me that he would find out all he could about the affair and let me know the outcome. Two days later, he arrived at Issy-les-Moulineaux.

"My dear friend," he told me, "I'm terribly sorry, but your car is indeed in my workshops, in bits. No doubt thousands of things escape your notice in your factory; in mine, I'm constantly in conflict with over-zealous people. As you know, our technical service has examples of all the best cars on the market, and your 10CV is one such; our 'indiscretion' department acquired it..."

"But how do you explain the price of this transaction?" I replied.

Louis Renault told me the exact circumstances under which the 10CV of the *Circuit des Routes Pavées* had disappeared. Four major manufacturers had wanted to acquire this car that three months earlier had met with what seemed to them such inexplicable success, and the resulting auction had led to the exorbitant price.

This episode hurt me greatly. The Peugeot company, so powerful and respected, hadn't hesitated to plagiarise one of our models on the basis of plans acquired by dubious means; and here was Louis Renault, to whom I would have gladly given all the information he wanted about our ironmongery, tolerating a despicable deceit as if it were no great surprise!

I had quite a high opinion of myself, more's the pity. This was not based on my work, my circumstances or my success, but on the conviction that I was someone to be reckoned with - a well-informed man of the world, whereas I was evidently just a naïve fool, as vainly pretentious as I was incorrigibly stupid.

One of my administrators whom I considered a complete idiot took the ridiculous precaution of personally burning the contents of his wastepaper basket every day - an action which always seemed to me to be the height of stupidity. These events changed my mind - but I still could not work on the basis of assuming that people I respected would do wrong.

There was more to life than these distressing incidents, however. The rigours of the motor trade were from time to time punctuated by much hilarity. One of my oldest and dearest friends, Henry Kapferer,[10] a former aviator who in the heroic age had piloted dirigibles, was of course a Voisin owner. Henry was hard of hearing, an affliction that played cruel tricks upon him.

One day in 1925, my old chum came into my garret looking tired and drawn. Thinking at first he was ill, I bade him make himself comfortable before telling me his troubles. He got straight to the point. Like all self-respecting Frenchmen, Henry was car-mad.

"Come and see my car," he said. "It has a device on the transmission side which isn't on my brother's Voisin. Have you by any chance fitted some new mechanism to mine?"

Reassuring my old friend, I followed him out. The car looked perfectly normal. Henry invited me to inspect the underside, where I did indeed see an unusual structure squashed up between the back axle and the floor. On further investigation, the nature of the 'new device' became apparent. It was a folding metal garden chair which, having been collected at some speed, had crumpled up beyond recognition...

---

10) A founder member of the Automobile Club de France and commissaire of the Aéro Club de France (which he co-founded), **Henri Kapferer** built and flew 44 airships while running the Astra company belonging to his uncle, the Shell oil tycoon Henri Deutsch. In 1906, he came to *Les Frères Voisin* workshop to order components for the dirigible *Ville de Paris*, and commissioned the first Voisin cellular biplane the following year. One of the greatest blimp pilots in Europe, it was to Kapferer that Nieuport turned to build his first aeroplane in 1908; at the time GV is writing of, he was still technical director of Nieuport Astra. Kapferer later founded the *Compagnie Générale Transaérienne*, which became Air France.

The 'Kapferer case' was taken to the nearby assembly shop to be put on as hoist for the ironmongery to be removed. Henry absolutely insisted on it being a special modification, and was only convinced otherwise when I managed to unfold what remained of the chair. It was easy to deduce what must have happened. Louts had thrown the chair from one of the terraces in the Tuileries, and lying flat in the road, it had been 'swallowed' by the driver who, being deaf, noticed nothing unusual...

A week later, a man I didn't know showed me with a second-hand 18CV which had run a main bearing. The car had left the factory when our bearings were splash lubricated, before full pressure lubrication was standard. The oil was pumped into four troughs across the crankcase. A scoop on each bearing collected oil from these troughs to lubricate the bearing through the orifice provided and also the surrounding moving parts. Although the resulting lubrication was by nature somewhat haphazard, there were usually dire consequences whenever a careless mechanic removed the filter from the oil filler opening to save time when replenishing the engine oil. Any foreign body falling into the crankcase could easily insinuate itself into one of the troughs, where it would be trapped by the scoop and damage the trough in such a way as to allow the oil to escape.

This is what had happened to the engine I was asked to inspect. But the owner was adamant in his insistence that the filter had not been removed.

"I lubricate my car myself," he said, "and take all the proper precautions."

I had the engine dismantled on the spot, and within a few minutes the sump lay at our feet. Fragments of one of the troughs could be seen in the oil, but not the offending component itself. Just as we were about to admit defeat in the face of our client's protestations,

I spotted a small object folded back on itself in the corner of the sump. I picked it up before the plaintiff's eyes and dipped it in petrol. It was his gold wedding band...

Having probably been a little oversized, it had slipped off this great mechanic's ring finger during an oil change. The King of the Road was flabbergasted. His face suddenly brightening, he leaned over and confided in a suddenly friendly tone:

"You've done me a great service! My wife has been giving me hell for the past week about losing my wedding ring..."

It would take several weighty tomes to recount all the tales of the car-buying public. One day I was visited by a very amiable fellow who explained that as his business often took him as far afield as Marseilles and Bordeaux, he had to travel at night when it was often quite difficult to refuel. Having tried several makes, both French and foreign, he found that our 18CV had pretty much satisfied his requirements.

Almost immediately, I had sketched out a possible solution on my drawing board, though a difficult one to realise. This nocturnal traveller wanted to cover Paris-Nice in twelve to fourteen hours. Nothing would dissuade him from this objective, inspired by the past triumphs of Lamberjack, whose official time for this journey was eleven and a half hours.

At the time, I didn't have a chassis that could achieve this feat with a full complement of passengers and luggage. My visitor then told me that he had seven or eight friends who would be definite customers for any vehicle that managed to meet his requirements. It then became merely a question of money, and my interlocutor suggested a sum that would cover the costs of building a prototype.

The challenge attracted me. It was however a mistake, since by accepting it I joined the ranks of bespoke manufacturers, whose efforts are never adequately remunerated.

I consulted my most senior salesman, Rivière, who gave me more details. The man I had just met owned several brothels in Paris, the provinces and abroad...

'Mr Louis' was, it seemed, an exacting customer and something of a connoisseur. He was also a man of impeccable financial probity. I took the project seriously, and our enthusiast not only paid a very considerable sum, but also brought us five of his friends who also placed valuable orders.

By this stage, I had fully mastered the profession I loved. I began designing a six-litre, six-cylinder engine[11] based on our 18CV. This six had a cast aluminium block (without liners, since our outer sleeves could run directly against aluminium), and was rated as a 33CV by the *Service des Mines*. Despite its lightness, this was an indomitable brute of an engine which we were later to push to its very limits. At 2,500rpm, our 33CV faultlessly produced 130bhp for eight days and nights in complete safety and without a single hiccough. A gearbox was quickly designed, and I placed two 100-litre fuel tanks on either side of the drive shaft.[12] Six months after Mr. Louis' first visit, we were ready.

Our 33CV was a great success. Its very direct steering was precise, if a little heavy, and though not undergeared, absolutely devoid of shimmy and other reactions. The brakes were excellent; the suspension quite hard, but not unacceptably so. Roadholding was excellent.

---

11) With the slightly shorter (94mm) stroke of the C9 *Laboratoire*, the dry sump C16 engine displaced 5,830cc. The main con rods and those actuating the sleeves were tubular; the crankshaft ran in three huge main bearings, and induction was via twin Zenith DU42 carburettors.

12) The C16 was based on the chassis of the 1926 C12, which had a single fuel tank to one side of the torque tube.

The enormous size of the 24CV and 33CV Voisins is not evident from most photographs of factory-bodied cars.

Three days after delivering our first 33CV, I was visited by a friend of 'Mr Louis' who had just driven from Paris to Bordeaux in the company of the man who had first inspired our development programme.

"My dear Mr Voisin," he said, "We left Paris at eight in the evening. By the time we reached Etampes, I needed to stop for my less than obliging bladder. But my driver put me at ease: 'Piss in your clothes, because you'll be wetting yourself throughout the journey; I'm not stopping before we get to Bordeaux.' We arrived at two in the morning; when at last I was able to get out of the car, drenched from head to toe."

Our 33CVs were excellent and commercially successful cars. I became attached to this rather unusual clientèle, both forthright and loyal, and in my entire career I have met few people as meticulous, open and reasonable as they were.

Chapter VIII

In 1923, our plans were well advanced to compete again in the *Grand Prix du Tourisme* of the Automobile Club de France, certain of completely thrashing our competitors. During the year I had shaved nearly 100 kilos from our victorious 1922 car, and the streamlined mudguards we had designed easily added an extra five or six kph to the top speed.

As in every year, the rules of the event took a long time to appear. When they eventually did, everything led me to suppose that the sporting commission of the ACF had somehow been circumvented, and we were being targeted directly. The regulation in question (which furthermore had no successor) required competitors to fit a forward-facing flat panel to the rear of their cars so as to render any vestige of aerodynamics utterly futile. It can only be wondered how such a grotesque imbecility can be proposed, discussed and agreed by a body of people of whom one would expect at least a little discernment...

On the 10th of July 1923, I wrote an open letter to the Automobile Club de France, which appeared in the press. I expressed my astonishment at the singular procedures by which they proposed to stimulate progress in the French motor industry, and announced that our firm would be abstaining from this meaningless contest. But to ensure that this withdrawal could not be considered an admission of defeat, I finished the letter with a challenge. In effect, I declared that although we would take no part in the *Grand Prix de Tourisme*, we would compete in the racing category instead: "We have barely six months in which to achieve an overwhelming financial and technical feat, in the certainty of being beaten. But we have the firm expectation of showing low-powered cars designed for speed."

4 "Voisin" du Grand Prix devant leur ravitaillement .
Tours 2 Juillet 1923.

This impulsive commitment was the height of folly. We had absolutely nothing in our archives, or in our design studies, or in the equipment at our disposal to create even the semblance of a car capable of competing in this race, and at Tours we would be facing the best-prepared and most experienced specialists in pure speed. The engine required had to be a two-litre, which we had never envisaged. Now, 38 years on, when I think of my recklessness of 1923, I still painfully ask myself how on earth we managed to take part in this Tours Grand Prix after only six months of work.

I had on various occasions sketched out designs for highly specialised cars inspired by the fuselage of our aeroplanes, which despite weighing only 40 kilos, could nevertheless accommodate 300 horsepower engines. I had conceived of a chassisless design, constructed solely from fabricated panels, to which the engine and suspension could be mounted directly. This was the principle I introduced for Tours, creating in the process the first monocoque of the type now adopted the world over.

The concept had two great advantages. It was the lightest possible way to build a car. It was completely rigid, and we stood to gain considerable time by not being dependent on externally sourced chassis pressings.

Assisted by my two stalwarts Lefebvre and Bernard, a timetable was prepared in 48 hours allowing for preliminary trials of a 13CV engine producing 70bhp at 3,000rpm. A week later, the body was completed. Consisting of a framework of 30 x 30mm ash spars clad in aluminium, it weighed 38 kilos.

We could use the front axle our 13CV, and the 'truncated' transmission was lodged in the rear. The car had unequal track: 500mm at the rear, 1,350mm at the front. I conducted tests

Grand Prix Vitesse A·C·F· _ Tour 2 Juillet 1923 _ Rougier en Vitesse

with André Lefebvre. The car surpassed all our expectations. Its aerodynamic efficiency was unexpectedly good, but lateral stability was less so. On the way back from Villacoublay, Lefebvre rolled the car on its right (without damage) at the bend by the Post Office at Issy.

The rear track was widened little by little, and we were finally satisfied with its lateral stability at 750mm, which could still be accommodated within the rear of our bodywork.

The two-litre engine was then constructed. It was a six-cylinder, with aluminium block of course, and we increased the number of measures taken to lower upper cylinder temperatures, but despite its high compression ratio, our engine never exceeded 75bhp at 4,000rpm. This lack of power was to cause us difficulties. Despite the excellent aerodynamics, our cars never exceeded 175kph, whereas the Sunbeams[1] approached 200kph.

Of the eighteen cars entered for the Tours Grand Prix, only five crossed the finishing line. Thirteen of our competitors, including some of the greatest names in racing, bit the dust.[2] We were at least among the survivors.

This exceptionally tough race, which had cost us so much effort and sacrifice, had no effect on our sales. Our clientèle quite rightly saw little connection between an out-and-out racing machine and a touring car, a view reinforced by the fact that the singular appearance of our Tours cars bore no resemblance whatsoever to the cabriolets which were then all the rage...

---

1) Sunbeams finished 1st 2nd and 4th at Tours, with Segrave's winning car covering the 800 kilometres at an average 75mph. Louis Coatalen had poached Walter Becchia and Fiat's Vincent Berrarione to design the 102bhp twin-cam six, which was modelled on Nazzarro's victorious Fiat 804 of the previous year.

2) Including the sophisticated twin-cam Rolland Pilains, the Fiats, a Delage and all the Bugattis except Friedrich's third place car. Although 75 minutes behind the winning Sunbeam, Lefebvre brought *Laboratoire* No.10 into 5th place at an average of 63.2mph - not bad for a 65bhp car in a 500-mile race that claimed 13 of the 18 starters. Duray and Rougier, in No.5 and 15 respectively, retired; André Morel in No.17 was disqualified. The *Laboratoire* was timed at over 105mph. In the touring car category, Boillot took first honours in a clean sweep of Peugeot 174 Voisin clones.

American cars were beginning to pose a threat to our company. America exported so-called luxury cars to France, and my friend Barbezat[3], who sold Packards, was a worrying competitor.

The Americans' success could not have been due to the technical merit of what they produced. All three of the American cars I had tested with any seriousness had revealed irremediable defects. Snobbery was very much grist to the mill of our competitors, and the gullible were seduced by the names of foreign cars.

'Roadster', for example, had a particular appeal for our clientèle. Although we were asked for roadsters, I made the mistake of neglecting to meet this demand.

During a trip that took me to Mont Ventoux, where we had carried out trials of our hillclimb cars, I experienced a painful revelation. On an empty straight road in excellent condition on the outskirts of Vienne, in the Isère, my roadster-bodied car skidded before I had the chance to intervene. I ploughed across a ditch - luckily, not a very deep one - and just as I regained control of the car, I hit a dirt track and stopped, shocked by what had just happened.

My surprise at the suddenness of this phenomenon had prevented me from controlling my speed; I was probably driving at over 100kph. Quite a strong southerly wind was blowing along the Rhône valley, but at that point the road wasn't running parallel to the direction of the wind and the gust that had overwhelmed me was at about 20 degrees to my direction of travel.

3) **Maurice Barbezat** began his career as an engineer with Gobron-Brillié. After the war, he took over the defunct company's premises in Billancourt to import American cars and in 1924 became Packard's exclusive distributor in France, supplying locally bodied cars from plush showrooms on the Champs Élysées. Établissements Barbezat sold more than 200 Packards in 1930/31, but sales had tailed off to only 26 in 1932.

Accidents of this type have happened thousands of times - indeed, one cost Queen Astrid of Belgium her life while driving such a roadster.[4] They only become serious under certain conditions, when the loss of control results in a crash rather than a narrow escape. Even then, the incident is soon forgotten if only minor injuries are sustained.

In the chassis drawings we sent to coachbuilders and the comprehensive catalogues we published to coincide with the Salon, we set out a fully detailed explanation of the crucial question of 'centring'. To make our point clearly, we resorted to a 'funicular polygon',[5] whose main effect was to provoke ridicule from the car-buying public, most of whom are illiterate and remarkable mainly for their inexplicable pretentiousness.

At first, these extremely important and directly safety-related measures were strictly complied with, and just as the Rolls-Royce company imposes conditions on its coachbuilders, we frequently refused to issue our guarantee. Concerned by this ostracism, our sales department gradually relaxed the application of our technical instructions, and this relaxation extended to our own coachwork to the point that the roadster we built did not comply with our own stipulations.

As the car's centre of air pressure was ahead of its centre of gravity, it was thrown off balance by the side wind so suddenly that I was unable to catch it.

Returning to Paris, I tried to halt production of the Voisin roadster. I made my case as forcefully and persuasively as I could at our technical meeting, but to no avail. Clients who had ordered roadsters insisted upon having them, and the finance department depended

---

4) King Leopold III was driving Queen Astrid in a Packard 120 in the Alps in 1935 when the car plunged down a ravine.

5) This curious expression (which must refer to cable cars rather than cables) refers to the defiantly angular lightweight body styles with pronounced tumblehome which first clad Voisin chassis in 1923.

on these orders being fulfilled. Had they been constructed by other coachbuilders, I would certainly have refused to issue our guarantee, but as products of our own factory, I was trapped by my own negligence.

Though we never had a fatality, one of these roadsters caused an accident which resulted in a death and two very serious injuries. In a scenario which has unfortunately repeated itself a thousand times since 1924, the car was travelling along a straight, empty, well-surfaced road. The accounts of the two witnesses and the 12-year old child who saw the drama unfold were in complete agreement: the Voisin was driving at around 100kph, slightly to the right of the crown of the road when suddenly it slewed across the highway and collided with a tree. The child, whom I interviewed personally, assured me that "the car just flew into the tree".

The insurance 'experts' were pretty sure of finding a mechanical or chassis failure. I was present during the examination that followed, which revealed the mechanical elements to be intact. Driver illness was suggested, just as it is today, and that is how the cause of the incident was classified.

Removing the body from my roadster, I commissioned a 1/10th scale model for tests in the wind tunnel run by Colonel Lafay,[6] professor of physics at the École Polytechnique. The results were disastrous. Like a weather vane, that is to say with a vertical axis passing directly through the centre of gravity, my car spun instantly, just as it had done in my hands six months earlier outside Vienne, and as had been reported by the witnesses of our fatal accident.

I shall return to this subject of 'empennages' later, but I know that the obvious is one of the hardest things to prove.

---

6) GV had first worked with Lafay on the aerodynamics of a finned shell he designed in 1916.

In 1937 my old friend Henry Kapferer acquired a small Renault saloon, a miserable affair in which he offered to drive me to an appointment in Mâcon. It did its job adequately on the way there, but after throwing its fan belt in clouds of steam at Saulieu, we only just managed to reach the Renault agent for a repair.

How is it that a car should be incapable of functioning without this bit of string? Voisins never had fans under my technical direction,[7] yet I never received the slightest complaint from a single client on the subject.

The return journey from Mâcon to Paris in this Renault held another surprise in store for us. Driving confidently on an excellent road out of Fontainebleau, Henry overtook the inevitable lorry. Immediately after this manoeuvre, the Renault veered to the left, rolled over several times and after skidding between two trees, and came to rest on a pile of gravel. The lorry drivers behind us stopped, literally terrified. The two men couldn't believe their eyes, and without pausing to ask, began checking the steering, convinced that we were victims of some mechanical failure. There was nothing wrong with steering, as it turned out. The car was righted, restarted and we arrived in Paris without further incident.

We had brushed within a few centimetres of a plane tree that would have dispatched us both to our maker had the gods been less benign. I met my old friend three days later at the wheel of his jalopy, and realised when I reminded him of our escapade that he had completely forgotten what had led up to it.

This type of accident has nothing to do with indisposition on the part of either the driver or the state of the road, nor the highway code, nor the mechanical condition of the vehicle or

7) An oversight. GV refers here to models appearing after the 4-litre, which was equipped with a large three-bladed cast aluminium fan, as was the C2.

even tyre adhesion, which although capable of affecting controllability, absolutely cannot overcome such an instantaneous and irresistible phenomenon. Driver carelessness is not a factor.

This type of accident causes five or six deaths and some twenty injuries a day in France alone - in other words, a fifth of the daily toll of road accident victims. It would perhaps be wise to teach our automobile 'technicians' about the handling of a wardrobe on castors in the face of a 100-120kph wind, which in a typhoon is sufficient to lift the roofs of an entire town, flatten walls, uproot trees and sow widespread death and destruction in an instant.

Despite my repeated insistence on the matter, these observations will in all probability bear no fruit. As Einstein said, prejudices are harder to break than atoms.

The economic crisis was soon to wreak its havoc. Having known unbelievably good times, we were about to enter an era of insurmountable difficulties. Talking one day to Rivière, to whom I confided some of my anxieties, I asked his opinion of what could be done to help our company. His reply was brief and to the point: "You couldn't even give your cars away."

A little later, I saw something I had never seen before: rows of chassis without buyers in a building specially adapted for the purpose, the Hall Marceau.

We had to eat. A banker agreed to extend us credit facilities guaranteed against our stock. The interest payable on this arrangement absorbed what meagre profit we made, so our prices duly rose. Two fraudsters then proposed a disastrous purchase of our guarantees. The deal was done, and the fraudsters sold no cars.

The banks pressed harder and harder to obtain their pound of flesh. These gentlemen, who drove around at our expense in cars they had not bought, grew ever more rapacious. I was asked for personal guarantees.

I was married under the law of the separation of goods, and with the imprudence of the fool that I was, everything I owned was in my wife's name. One morning I asked her to sign the guarantee for an overdraft facility, and with an expression on her face I had never seen before, she refused...

I've experienced some cruel setbacks in my life and endured periods of real misery. But this refusal rendered me incapable of all rational thought. When I came to my senses, I took stock of the situation, dressed, took my hat and left the marital home without a word. I never went back on my decision. I sued for divorce. The divorce was not motivated by a desire for my freedom; that I already had. Our life together had been good - I would even add that my status as a married man often proved useful as a refuge, a pretext, an excuse, whenever I wasn't being carried away by some senseless desire in my chaotic private life. But I had been literally dumbfounded by my wife's refusal.

When I married her, Miss Bernet's life was blighted by her complete inability to live within her means. I'm now quite certain that my wife loved me, and I too loved her - but she was consumed by the pustulent canker of avarice, which ultimately proved stronger than all other feelings. I had the proof 12 years later when my sister-in-law Jeanne, whom I often saw, seduced me into an attempt at reconciliation. The date and time of the meeting were set, and I agreed to try one last time. I composed a letter to the effect that the trap for my wife's greed was but an empty gesture, as she already possessed all my worldly goods in any case. I sealed the letter and gave it to my sister-in-law, who knew nothing of what it contained, and awaited the meeting as arranged. My ex-wife, whom I had not seen for 12 years, entered the drawing room in the presence of the sister. She sat down facing me and in an even voice I told her that I had a question to ask before considering our reconciliation:

"Are you prepared to return what you took from me? You have ten seconds to give me your answer..."

I was expecting an outburst, tears, a lecture. But no answer came from her lips. I then asked my sister-in-law if she would be kind enough to open my letter and read it to the party concerned. I rose and left the room.

I moved into boulevard Exelmans alone on leaving the conjugal home in the boulevard d'Auteuil.[8] I organised my life in this house which had been conceived solely for my own pleasures, and worked every day at Issy where we thought up a thousand and one ways to try and overcome our troubles.

The question of 'demonstrations' arose once more. The ACF *Grand Prix de Tourisme* was to be run at Lyon, with three categories: A (full size cars), B (medium) and C (light cars).

I entered two cars in group A,[9] and one each in groups B and C. Rougier and Gaudermann were to drive in group A.

8) According to Noel Bilger, the nephew who was living there at the time, GV left the marital home years after the 1924 Grand Prix, in 1928 at the earliest.

9) Three cars were in fact entered in this category, the third (no.39) being driven by **Omberto Piccioni** (a friend of Rougier's who had previously campaigned Steyrs in France).

Our group B car was in the hands of Morel,[10] a very able driver. Finally, André Lefebvre was to drive the group C car.

A few weeks before the Lyon Grand Prix, a sports journal of the time had published an article entitled 'Scandal at the ACF Grand Prix'. This 'scandal' was, it seems, provoked by our chassisless Voisins. I had indeed applied to our Lyon cars the same construction method I had first used at Tours. The Voisins that were to compete in the ACF *Grand Prix de Tourisme* were conceived in the form of an aircraft fuselage, in aluminium of course, freeing us from the constraints of an antiquated chassis. In a word, I had applied the monocoque principles that are nowadays universally adopted.

But the cry of 'scandal' had struck a chord with the many idiots our old firm then employed, and their influence militated against my most categorical pronouncements. This disorderly state of affairs allowed certain undesirable features to be introduced, and our cars for the Grand Prix differed considerably in detail. This lack of discipline was to cost us victory, and I have never forgiven myself for my weakness in dealing with people who abuse the trust I place in them.

Rougier had arranged a profitable deal on his own account with a carburettor company, so his car differed from the others. I had constructed a bombproof four-litre engine. A much stronger crankshaft with larger crank pins was far less mechanically efficient than our 18CV, but yielded 130bhp at 3,500rpm.

---

10) After joining Jules Salomon at Le Zèbre in 1918, ex-Berliet engineer and test driver **André Morel** gave the marque its only win in 1921 before effectively co-founding Amilcar. Until he left in 1929, Morel was responsible for much of Amilcar's giant-killing successes in events as diverse as the *Bol d'Or*, Mont Ventoux, *Le Circuit des Routes Pavées,* the first 24-hour races at Le Mans and Spa, the *Tour de France Auto* and Brooklands 200 mile races. From 1933, he ran the competition department at Talbot.

I have to say that I've never driven a combustion-engined car comparable to these group A cars. The race had two parts: an endurance test, conducted at night, with a speed trial the following day.

Rougier lost 33 minutes at the start of the endurance test as a result of the carburettor he had imposed on us, and which must have earned him a comfortable sum. I was tearing my hair out. Having flattened the batteries in vain attempts to start the engine, our champion struggled breathlessly with the starting handle with no greater success. His engine was flooded, and I eventually persuaded him to remove the spark plugs and turn over the engine before replacing them.

The car finally started, but Rougier was agitated. He was no longer a young man. The time he had lost at the start and the penalties he had accrued by having had to start the engine on the handle had made him careless. He took risks during the night, and after entering a right-angled bend much too fast, he ended up in a ditch from which he could not extricate himself.

Gaudermann, our second group A driver, was ten minutes in the lead when a rear tyre burst, and he lost 20 minutes ineptly trying to change the wheel. Morel, in group B, would have saved the day had it not been for his right front wing flying off in a bend. Our suspension travel was limited for aerodynamic reasons, and when a touch of the front wheel forced the mudguard upwards, it tore away from the running board. Morel stopped and put the wing in the car, but he didn't anticipate our competitors' ploy that cost him his first place: an ACF commissaire in effect demanded that he replace the mudguard during the race. I was furious, but it was too late to talk reasonably to these people with whom we had already exchanged angry words.

Though a brilliant performance, the result of this race was for us a disappointment.
A single Peugeot - the Voisin in disguise - finished the race; the other two had spilled their guts on the circuit. But the survivor took first place - we had to content ourselves with second, third and fourth.[11]

These races, in which a marque's hopes could be dashed by the difference of a few seconds over 600 kilometres, exasperated me. The bad faith of our competitors enraged me.
I decided henceforth never to risk our good name in these pitiless struggles in which our loyalty and confidence were rewarded with kicks in the teeth, and I readied myself to take our chances in the arena of world records.

I realised that this was a desperate gamble, but I preferred to pit myself against soulless chronometers than constantly rubbing shoulders with unscrupulous chancers. Had we been able to afford the considerable expense involved in sending personnel and equipment to America, I wouldn't have hesitated for an instant; but we had at our disposition the Montlhéry Autodrome not far from our base, but whose bowl imposed on our drivers and cars the most terrifying cliff-like bends...

---

11) Morel brought the light 4-litre (no.12) to fourth in the 1000kg class after a trio of Cottin Desgouttes, and in the 1400kg class, Gaudermann (no.37) and Piccioni (no.39) came second and third respectively after d'Auvergne's Peugeot.

Chapter IX

Only those who have driven flat out at over 200kph for 24 hours around the Montlhéry banking are qualified to pass judgement on performances of this type.

Our world record for 24 hours at an average speed of 182.66kph stood for seven years, and was only beaten on the uniquely extensive and well-equipped course at Salt Lake City.[1]

Furthermore, the difficulty of what we had achieved that day is evinced by the fact that 30 years later in 1961, the winner of the celebrated Le Mans 24 Hours only beat our time by ONE kph, and that on a perfect track with long straights. Without mentioning what little progress the automobile industry had been able to make in 30 years, I would however point out that the 5-litre Chevrolet Corvettes never equalled our average speeds.[2]

Naturally, we planned preliminary tests before summoning the FIA and its timekeepers. These semi-clandestine attempts ought to have discouraged us. Despite the quality of the concrete, the surface of the Montlhéry oval was as rough as a stormy sea at 200kph, and none of our machines could withstand more than an hour at full speed. I won't mention our engines, whose elegantly scattered internals decorated the track, nor the transmissions whose bearings would disintegrate after 40 minutes. I shall speak only of the axles and suspension, the handling, tyres and wheels.

---

1) Voisin's record run took place at Montlhéry on September 27th, 1927, and was finally broken in 1935, at 137.4mph (134.8 according to some sources) by Cobb, Rose-Richards and Dixon in the Napier-Railton on Bonneville Salt Flats.

2) Although the point remains valid, Gendebien and Hill's winning Ferrari 250TR in fact averaged 186.53kph, and under race conditions on a street circuit rather than a banked oval. No Corvettes took part in 1961, but Fitch and Grossman had finished 8th in the previous year's race at an average 157.6kph.

La 18 ch. Voisin 4 cyl. S.S. de 3^{ce} 980 de cylindrée qui a battu, à Montlhéry, le 23-9-25 les deux records du monde, toutes catégories, des 6 heures et des mille Km à 161 ^{k}694 de moyenne et dix records internationaux class C. Lefebvre, Marchand et Julienne conduisant alternativement.

Lefebvre (in white) stands with co-drivers Marchand and Julienne beside the first of the Voisin record-breakers in the autumn of 1925. With an engine based on one of the Lyon GP cars (according to Bellu), the 118bhp four-litre and its radiator were mounted further aft. By November, the car had taken five world records including the six hours (at some 172kph). It returned to the track (with 22 more horsepower) the following February, by which time the competition from Renault, Panhard and others was increasing.

It was difficult at that time to prepare a car weighing less than 1100 kilos for a 24-hour world record. For three hours' running, the fuel alone weighed some 100 kilos. The engine was a four-litre 18CV four-cylinder producing 150bhp at full power. Our axles and suspension were production items, with conventional leaf springs.

Contrary to expectations, our car ran at 200kph, high against the retaining wall of the near-vertical banking, and in their determination to better their lap times, our drivers would enter these bends on the inside of the track and 'climb the cliff' in such a way as to generate sudden and unpredictable centrifugal forces that negated all our precautions by effectively doubling the weight of machine and driver.

In other words, our suspension components, designed for 1,200 kilos, suddenly had to cope with 2,400. The springs collapsed under the load, the axles hit the chassis and the battering began, steadily destroying the machinery like a power hammer.

The exit of the North turn whcrc it flowed into the short straight that preceded the second turn was dangerously dependent on a degree of precision that precluded steering corrections. A good friend, Cozette,[3] had killed himself on this section of the track a few days before our first tests.

---

3) This accident in fact occurred four years after the first Voisin record runs, on August 20th, 1929. Having filed his first carburettor patent at the age of 20 in 1915, the talented pilot and driver **René Cozette** consolidated his reputation by resolving high altitude carburetion problems and founded the Société du Carburateur Cozette in 1919. After moving to the US to collaborate with spark plug and magneto entrepreneur Albert Champion, he returned to expand his operations to include manufacturing Ricardo-type cylinder heads and eccentric vane superchargers that boosted the output of many proprietary-engined vintage sports cars. As one of the pioneers (with Marcel Violet) of 2-stroke engines for cars in the early 20s and co-designer of the 1925 sleeve valve Guyot racing engines, Cozette in 1926/7 developed his own 1100cc opposed-piston 2-stroke four cylinder with eight pistons, two crankshafts and complex spur gears. This extraordinary power unit was mounted in a car of his own design in which he lost his life in a 200kph accident thought to have been caused by a failure of the car's chain steering during the Montlhéry record attempt GV mentions.

Inset: Lefebvre and Bernard based the second record car on the 4.9-litre six-cylinder prototype of the forthcoming C12, with twin carbs and a higher compression ratio, a narrower, underslung chassis with no front brakes, yet it proved hardly more powerful than its predecessor and little faster. It took only the 50-mile and 50- and 100-kilometre records.

Above: The replacement GV specified for 1927 was altogether more mettlesome, a 7,938cc straight eight consisting of two GP de Lyon C5 blocks yoked together on a common crankcase and offset by about 10cms. Massive oil radiators below each side of the crankcase were fed by louvres in the undertray. A Y-shaped aluminium manifold connected the two nearside Zeniths to a big Tecalemit air filter. To save weight, the car only had direct drive. Wheel discs were used only at the back, as they upset the steering when fitted to the front. After unsuccessful trials with Michelins, the Rudge wheels were shod with treadless 33" x 5.35" SS Dunlops. Fuel and oil tanks in the long tail were sufficient for 90 minutes flat out, and the start line weight with driver was 1370kg. No lights were fitted, GV having illuminated the track with acetylene searchlights. Initially, Marchand averaged 127.54mph for the 100 kilometres and knocked 30 seconds off Eldridge's 100-mile record (in a blown 2-litre Miller), at 128.55mph. 'The hour' was GV's aim, but one of the rear Dunlops was seen to be wearing unduly and the car was called in 12 minutes before time. Later, he covered 128 miles in an hour. With Morel relieving Marchand every 90 minutes and Kiriloff held mainly in reserve, the big Voisin took world honours up to six hours at 116.1mph prior to lifting the 24-hour record to 113.4mph (2,724 miles). A higher gear ratio was later adopted to reduce rpm from 2,600-3,000 to about 2,000. So well did the Dunlops hold up that instead of changing them all at each stop, the rears were changed every three hours; the offside front was replaced after six hours, its companion every seven and a half hours (runs at Montlhéry being anti-clockwise). The car was sold to the Buenos Aires Voisin dealer Jack Vengerow for Marchand to drive in Argentina. Its fate is unknown.

Once again, we had neither the time nor the resources to devise an elegant solution to all these problems. The flexing of our overloaded standard production axles made the steering imprecise, and the car as a whole tore itself apart through stresses and strains that proved difficult to identify. Last of all, tyres weren't then what they are now, and lasted three hours at the most. As to the wire wheels - absolutely essential in our case - the spokes would pass straight through the rims!

Discouragement overtook us. The *Laboratoire* team began to lose hope, and at one stage I thought we would give up on the idea of world records altogether. I summoned a meeting between Lefebvre, Bernard and myself. The record programme was duly halted and we began rethinking the entire project.

We needed an engine, a lighter car and suspension specifically designed to accommodate very considerable load variations. We had the engine - a 6-litre 33CV six from which we managed to extract 180bhp within three weeks of the meeting.

We anticipated seven refuelling stops for the 24-hour world record, during which we had to change all the wheels, fill the tank with 100 litres of petrol, check the lubricants and steering and set off again. I decided to place our refuelling station beside the finish line, and therefore the timekeepers. Every three hours there would as a result be a lap that seriously compromised our average speed. It followed that we would lose very little more time by starting off in direct drive with the aid of an energetic push from our pit crews, instead of using our four-speed gearbox.

I therefore eliminated the gearbox entirely, and with it any worries about the bearings and gear selection mechanism.

Above: By the end of 1927, the 8-cylinder had covered itself in glory, with no less than 17 world records including the 24 hours. It duly took pride of place on that year's stand at the Paris Salon. In January 1928, it proceeded to capture the 10-mile record at 215kph; it also ran at Lugano in July, Marchand narrowly escaping death when the offside rear tyre flew off its rim and the skid that followed ripped off a front tyre as well. This caused the car to veer into the upper retaining wall, some 50 yards of which were demolished before the car eventually went through – fortunately, at a spot where the drop the other side was only a few feet.

Lastly, I adopted for our record cars a 'Présidence' type of clutch,[4] whose multiple surfaces were air-cooled. This gearless arrangement reduced the weight by 54 kilos and allowed us to shorten the car by some 40 cms, thereby considerably increasing our margin of safety.

This decision led to another. The track, crudely set at 1.4m, was reduced to 1.1m; steering lock was effectively unnecessary for the turns of a banked oval. By making the dimensions more compact in this way, we lost 90 kilos in weight and gained the rigidity we needed: halving the length of a pencil, ruler or axle QUADRUPLES its strength. The suspension was finalised as an arrangement of superimposed leaf springs, some of which came into play under conditions of overload - an arrangement which is nowadays adopted on many heavy goods vehicles. A preliminary 12-hour test of the car took place without incident.

As the track had to be lit at night, I acquired from a scrap merchant a mobile generator and lighting rig which feebly illuminated the Autodrome.

Our car was lubricated by an excellent oil, Yacco. The Yacco company came to our aid and covered all the lubrication and other costs. A week later, we were officially on the track. The FIA timekeepers set their stopwatches and I gave the order to start. Our average speed was 198kph after the 14th hour, when the radiator, despite being constructed to an exceptionally high specification by my old friend Dufour of the Chausson company, sprang a major leak.

Chassis flex complicated everything. Under constant battering and longitudinal torsion, the radiator brackets had torn away the radiator shell and I halted the run. But the records for 10 kilometres at 211kph, 100 kilometres at 205kph and 1,000 kilometres at an average speed of 186kph were ours!

---

4) Presumably a reference to special clutches fitted to the fleet of ceremonial 4-litre Voisins supplied to the state for official use by the President, senior ministers and visiting dignitaries.

Right: Financial constraints meant that Voisin's last record car (for an attempt on the 50,000 kilometres) was based on a production model - a 4.8 litre V12 with the factory's *Chatelaine* coupé body, with wings removed and additional fuel tanks replacing the rear trunk. Fuelled by the same 70/30 petrol/benzol mix as before, the attempt took place in September 1930, with César and Edouard Marchand, Van Doorninck and factory test driver Louis Le Roy de Présalé sharing stints at the wheel. The car ran for more than 17 days, breaking every target record in the process. Having secured every world record from 100 to 50,000 kilometres, as well as those from one hour to 17 days, Voisin retired from record breaking in Autumn 1930 covered in glory.

Above: Geo Ham's watercolour of the straight eight thundering round the lit banking at night, exhaust stubs flaming.

Such numbers are far removed from those that come to mind for sufferers from 'mad car disease'. But applied to real routes like Paris-Nice, these speeds would allow the journey to be accomplished in five hours, allowing for refuelling and tyre changes.

An arrangement of rubber spacers, together with longer hoses, gave us a 'floating' radiator - and a few days later, we renewed our assault on the world 24-hour record. My recollections aren't precise enough to be able to remember the exact speed we had to beat, but I think that it must have been nearly 160kph. It was therefore unnecessary to lap at 208kph to capture the record, so we set our speed at between 191 and 200kph.

The infernal round began yet again. Every three hours, we replenished the fuel, oil and water, during which all four wheels would be changed. The car would then be dragged backwards 50 metres and push-started.

Our world 24-hour record was homologated at an average speed of 182.6kph, which in fact involved lapping at over 200kph all day and for an unending night.[5]

Great success as it was, this type of victory only serves as a basis for the publicity campaign that follows such exploits. Our financial position precluded the exorbitant expense of proclaiming our achievements *ubi et orbi*.

The long-drawn process of preparing the record cars had led me to neglect the factory and our products. Fortunately, Bernard then took the initiative to increase the capacity of our six-cylinder from 2.5 to 3 litres. With good tuning and the addition of two twin-choke Zenith carburettors, it delivered 100bhp at 3,000rpm.

---

5) 26th September 1927.

Above: A pre-production prototype of the 17CV C23 that customers could buy, with the *Char* razor-edged '*angles vifs*' body style so characteristic of the factory's output at this period.

The 13CV thus became a 17CV,[6] the chassis was underslung, and with appropriate coachwork, the car easily reached 140kph. With virtually perfect steering, excellent roadholding and adequate brakes, it generated enough orders for us to survive a full-blown depression, had certain unproductive elements been rigorously culled.

The unproductive elements in question were unfortunately the heads of department, who had abundantly surrounded themselves with their own creatures. It was impossible for me to take action, and I waited - I waited for a miracle that couldn't happen. I was 57 years old...

We made no profit from our record-breaking activities, commercially speaking, but the Yacco company whose oil had lubricated our engines did exploit our achievements. This publicity must have worked, because within a few weeks of our 24-hour run, Yacco asked if we would be prepared to undertake attempts of hitherto unprecedented duration.

As the recession continued, my *laboratoire* was under threat from the well-known phenomenon whereby an organisation in financial difficulty never eliminates its unproductive elements but has no hesitation in sacking ordinary workers. Ensconced in their plethora of 'services', these gentlemen remained invulnerable, pausing only to draw their salaries and making it impossible to redress a difficult situation.

By providing the means to build a new prototype, Yacco came to the rescue of the *laboratoire* for the time being. I gratefully accepted their proposal and started work on a new design. It was no longer a matter of sustaining speeds in excess of 200kph, but of

6) The 17CV C23 was introduced in 1931, four years after the 24-hour record and a year after the final Voisin record runs; the C24 referred to here was a twin-carburettor underslung model that appeared two years later, in 1933.

Above: Using the 12-litre V12 constructed from two C18 six-cylinder blocks on a welded steel crankcase in a bid to achieve 25,000 miles at 100mph, the 1930 record attempts were well organised, with heaters for fresh sump oil, track illumination via red lamps powered by their own generators, and a doctor in permanent attendance. The inferior benzol fuel meant that the huge engine had to be rebuilt twice during the run. Two different tail treatments were tried. Although GV vehemently denied that the V12 "finished in worn out condition after the replacement of major parts" in a letter he wrote to the press in October 1929, but WF Bradley recounted otherwise in his *Motor Racing Memories:* "After a famous series of long-distance records on Montlhéry track, I asked him (GV) if they had changed many parts. "Changed many parts?" came the tart reply. "Why Sir, we changed everything on that car except the crankshaft!"

withstanding 14 days and nights at around 160kph. In other words, the endeavour we were embarking on represented around 300 hours of continuous driving, covering a distance of nearly 50,000 kilometres in the process - a performance that could only be achieved by fundamentally redesigning the whole car.

To complicate the situation, we had to use benzole instead of petrol. The Gaz de Paris company held vast stocks of this miserable fuel at the time, which they offered us in exchange for the publicity value of being associated with the attempt.

The results of our first trials were pitiful. We began by joining two of the four-litre four cylinder Lyon motors in line. They were excellent powerplants, light and robust enough for any endeavour. But running on benzole, these two units, looking like a very large straight eight, weren't much more powerful than our six-litre 24-hour record engines.

The infernal round began once again, this time accompanied by very dense exhaust smoke. We had not had time to adjust the compression to allow total combustion of benzole, which was duly completed outside the combustion chambers in the form of smoke and flames.

After three days and nights of battle, one of our front wheels collapsed on the North banking, its spoke nuts having penetrated the rim. I was there when the accident happened. The car listed heavily to the left, with only the hub remaining on the stub axle, and Kiriloff, our charming young driver,[7] was slightly injured. The car was a write-off. We obviously had to abandon our attempt, but I managed to design a new machine which was completed in a few weeks. By assembling two of our 33CV six cylinder blocks in a V configuration on a crankcase of arc-welded steel, I created a 12-litre V12.

7) **Serge Kiriloff** was one of the firm's export representatives who in 1943 (together with the Pierre Maubousson) patented a pioneering *canard* jet aeroplane design similar to the Concorde-like concept sketched by GV a few years later.

We had nothing capable of measuring this monster's output at Issy-les-Moulineaux. It probably yielded around 250bhp with ease at low engine speeds. Still without a gearbox, but with a clutch of bronze-steel discs, the hellish round began once more...

By the end of 1928, we held 37 officially homologated world speed records for automobiles, covering times from one hour to 16 days. The 16 days had been at an average of 121kph over a distance of 50,000 kilometres. 30 years later, some of these records have never been beaten. This explains why recent attempts by modern cars, unable to sustain a 121kph average for 16 days, have to exceed 50,000 kilometres in order to enter the record books.

We should have done much better, had not the use of benzole obliged us to rebuild the engine twice, thereby reducing our speed to the pathetic average of 121kph. This was despite having everything ready in advance for the rebuilds - two highly trained teams, their hands protected by asbestos gloves, stripped our V12, with its red hot manifolds, in the blink of an eye. Unfortunately, reassembly took precious time. On each occasion, we had to reset the junk head rings afresh, a highly exacting task which alone took an interminable hour's work.

To sum up, this world record battle proved from every point of view to be a marvellous training ground for my technical department. The construction of a Voisin was always rigorously disciplined, but I believe that without our 18 world records, the few very old cars of our marque which still now pass unnoticed among moderns would long since have vanished. In 1960 I made the journey from Paris to Nice with a 17CV Voisin. I encountered few cars able to overtake me during the entire length of the *route du soleil*, and despite intolerable traffic congestion, I was able to complete the 1,000-kilometre journey in 14 hours. My old black Voisin had given 30 good years of loyal service when it reached the *Promenade des Anglais*...

Chapter X

Our victory in the world records had little effect on sales, but considerably raised the profile of the Voisin technical department. My spiritual sons were little known in motoring circles, but after our exploits at Montlhéry, André Lefebvre and Marius Bernard each received lucrative offers from our competitors. My two friends, who lived very modestly and were under no illusions as to our prospects, replied that they preferred to remain with my company for personal reasons. I was of course profoundly touched by their loyalty, but I had no right to compromise the future of these big-hearted men. Their presence at my side had repercussions on the events which were to follow and the decisions I had to take.

After Montlhéry, I underwent a crisis similar to that which had led me to create our first 12-cylinder seventeen years earlier. Obsessed by two or three hobbyhorses of mine, I drew up three designs which were executed in the space of a few weeks. The first concentrated on aerodynamics. In the course of the long days of our record attempts, we had assimilated the requirements in terms of shape. Using 200bhp to drive at 200kph for 24 hours requires little intelligence; the real challenge is how to sustain such speeds with 50bhp. Though far from easy, this level of performance in itself presents no insuperable problems. At the design stage, one simply has to forget every precedent entirely.

Commercial considerations are fundamentally incompatible with revolutionary ideas. But with a few compromises, it was possible to construct something infinitely better than a cupboard on wheels. At the first attempt, I designed the car we were to call the Aérosport.

On a 17CV chassis, I had created the first pontoon body in the world.[1] Outdated as it may be, the term is easy to understand: until 1930, every car without exception consisted of a cabin, a bonnet and mudguards, which even carried the spare wheels. I entered the fray in 1925 by advocating the rear-mounted spare (a mistake, since it should in fact be mounted at the front). In my design, I aligned the body sides with the outer plane of the wheels, eliminating the mudguards entirely. Side and headlights were set into the body, and our radiator was integrated like that of a 1961 Mercedes 30 years later.

I assumed that this configuration would meet with no success whatsoever as far as our clientèle was concerned. I was mistaken. But it wasn't the 'pontoon' itself that convinced the buyers, but the increase in speed: the 17CV Aérosport achieved 150kph with 102bhp at 3,000rpm.

In other words, even though a client is often influenced by the so-called 'lines' of a car, that same client will immediately accept a revolutionary design if it delivers a real advantage.

I shan't mention our roofs that opened their entire length, actuated by a small vacuum motor[2], nor of our scuttle ventilation. Two or three of these cars still exist, one of which belongs to my old friend Antoine Menier. His Aérosport is in magnificent condition, and despite its 30 years, still does not look out of place among modern cars.[3]

---

1) The Aérosport's significance as a design landmark is attenuated by the fact that the company's dire financial situation didn't allow GV to alter the car's architecture to take advantage of the full-width effect, as Ledwinka and Übelacker did with the Type 77 Tatra of the same year (albeit with separate front wings).

2) See Compagnie Hellis patent 788.412 of July 1934.

3) The fourth generation heir to the chocolate dynasty, **Antoine Menier** (*top right, opposite page*) had owned Voisins since 1926, entering them in events for which he contrived various aerodynamic addenda and his own special exhaust system (he had patented various 'sonic camouflage' exhausts for making military aeroplanes sound like their enemy equivalents). The ex-Menier car is the only surviving Aérosport.

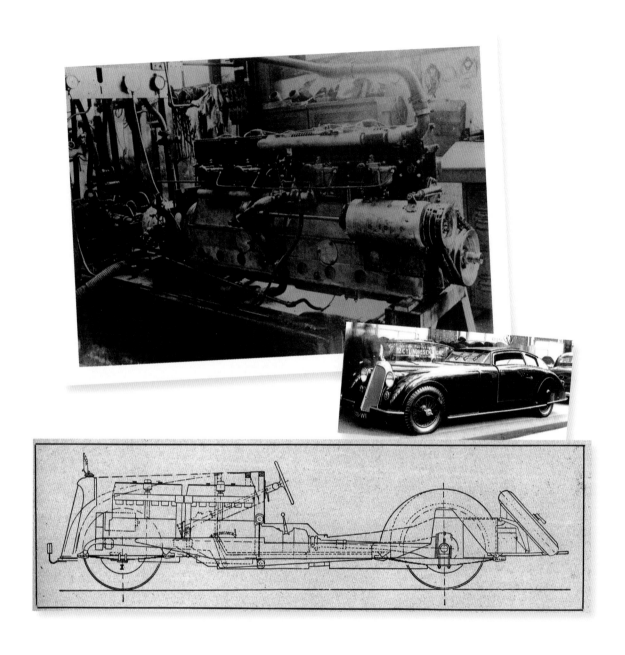

My second hobbyhorse, an extension of the first, was to attempt the world land speed record, which currently stands at around 600kph.[4] Of all the official world speed records, this is probably one of the easiest. There are impressive stockpiles of radial aeroplane engines to choose from. Though the car itself would obviously not resemble any one of our machines, the outcome is pretty much certain.

For some years, much has been spoken of our 'prestigious machines' whose importance is merely diplomatic. How can the France of Cugnot (1771) not beat the world land speed record for automobiles? The enterprise requires 10 kilometres of flat road - an aerodrome runway would very probably suffice.

My third hobbyhorse was a return to the V12. I had indeed constructed for my own personal use an Aérosport powered by an in-line twelve cylinder. Obviously, this engine protruded through the scuttle into the cabin somewhat, but no more shamefully than the small mountain inflicted on front passengers of these most excellent contrivances equipped with engines at the front whose drive is transmitted to the rear wheels - an arrangement already rejected by Cugnot almost 200 years ago!

My straight 12 was the result of assembling two 13CV engines in line. With a capacity of five litres, this phenomenon developed 150bhp at 3,000rpm, so the car (which I timed on several occasions at Montlhéry) could reach 170kph with two people on board. I often used it to drive between Paris and Mâcon.

At that time, Chryslers inexplicably found a few buyers in France. Although I don't enjoy racing on roads not closed for the purpose, I was very often overtaken on the Paris-Marseilles

4) John Cobb's 630.72kph record in the *Railton Mobil Special* at Bonneville in 1947 stood until 1960, when Mickey Thompson averaged 654.35kph in *Challenger 1*.

road by Chryslers, the driver or passengers making the small gesture familiar to so many imbeciles as they passed me at 110kph. I put up with such condescending adieus without reacting, but when it was accompanied by inane grimaces, I did on occasion let the car off its leash, and the Chryslers with their chrome-plated dummy valve covers would disappear in a blink, utterly thrashed.

Voisin customers, who had held the crown of the road for a good long time, hugely enjoyed these little dices. There being no question of heavy traffic at the time, our customers liked to annihilate their opponents, but our margin of speed was not sufficient to reduce the adversary to despair.

I frequently had to submit to such contests over 20 or 30 kilometres, evidently with mixed fortune. Those who engaged in these races, who for the most part considered themselves ace drivers, became careless and took serious risks - spoiling the journey for their wives and passengers, in other words.

The halcyon days of absolute dominance were over. It was clear that a car like my straight-12 would have easily put us back on the crown of the road. But it was another irrational reason that inclined me towards a five-litre V12...

As I have said, our last Montlhéry car was a 12-litre 12-cylinder;[5] perhaps the engine still exists in some museum of old cast-offs at Montlhéry. This monster of a car was obviously unusable by our clientèle, but it was a monster with certain attractive qualities. Terribly over-geared, the 50,000 kilometre machine ran at 1,000rpm per 100kph, so at 150kph, the big twelve was running at a leisurely 1,500rpm as if on an agreeable Sunday outing.

---

5) The penultimate record car is meant here; the last long distance record car was based on the production V12 in 1930.

Voisin 1931

198

I rolled up my sleeves and covered the drawing boards with plans for the five-litre twelve.[6]

To the men of our technical department, swept along as they were by all kinds of automotive banalities but firmly under my control, even an unusual design project came as welcome intellectual recreation. For those in the *laboratoire*, constructing a new prototype was fun; but for the unfortunates in the production department, a new type of car signalled the onset of major headaches...

At that time in our activities, our old company was far from brilliant on the technical side. The 12-cylinder was nevertheless built - a beautiful engine, silent, rapid and flexible. It was delivered in two forms - an 'ordinary' chassis that unfortunately lent itself to large, heavy coachwork, and an underslung chassis, whose rails were 20 cms from the ground.

On this chassis it was possible to build spacious cars with a roof height of only 1350mm. Amazed by the car's almost unprecedentedly low aspect, the public of 1936[7] persisted in believing that our 12-cylinder was too low to accommodate its occupants.

In fact, the bodies were identical to those which had been so admired when mounted on chassis rails 600mm from the ground, when they could only be entered via the intermediary of a running board...

6) In its first incarnation, this V12 was the 3.9 litre unit fitted to the C18 introduced in 1929; it was only in the following year that the power unit was enlarged to 4,885cc, in the 28CV C20.

7) A typographical error; GV is speaking of 1930, as the context makes clear.

One day in 1934 I received four Englishmen led by the head of the Rolls-Royce company.[8] Our conversation soon began:

"Monsieur Voisin, our company is very probably going to design and construct a 12-cylinder model," I was informed. "The four men in charge of our technical department and I have come from England to ask you if it would be possible to try one of your 12-cylinder cars, and to discuss with you what seem to us to be the thorny problems involved..."

I experienced one of the great moments of my life as a technician...

The visit from the Rolls-Royce company was of such a loyal and honourable character that I happily gave them all the information I could. To this delegation of the world's greatest mechanical engineers, I offered trials not only of the 12-cylinder I had under test, but also the Montlhéry monster.

A year later, Rolls-Royce introduced a 12-cylinder Phantom, which I was asked to try out. It is impossible not to admire such perfection unreservedly. Rolls Royce did of course have at its disposal a superbly trained and equipped technical department. But behind the prototypes, the Rolls factory could undertake fabrications which were unfortunately far beyond our means.

---

8) This delegation was probably led by W.A.Robotham, the former technical assistant to Ernest Hives, in one of his many factfinding missions to foreign manufacturers of luxury cars (together with R.W.Harvey-Bailey and perhaps Albert Elliott). If the date of this visit was indeed in 1934, the PIII 'Spectre' prototypes were by then already being road tested. It is thought that the introduction was made by battery magnate, author and automobilist Neville Minchin, a longstanding friend of Henry Royce who, while chairman of R-R's French concessionaire Franco-Britannic Automobiles, also had a big Voisin in his stable at the time. He was involved in the PIII development programme in that he was in 1935 given one of the first production models for evaluation. It is also worth noting that from the 'Eagle' series of aero engines in 1915 through its many successors (including the Type R and the Merlin), Rolls-Royce already had more experience of V12 engine design than any other firm.

I had worked long and suffered much for this great company of Issy-les-Moulineaux, but this gesture of Rolls Royce's made me completely forget the tribulations of the past.

Despite its evident accomplishments, our 12-cylinder 22CV sold poorly - and I have to say now that our clientèle was right. The car was fitted with a two-speed electromagnetic gearbox. A relay on the transmission permitted two further speeds, with the controls beneath the steering wheel. The desired combination could be selected with one finger; the only mechanical control was the lever which selected reverse.

It is quite inexplicable why and how this absolutely infallible and above all, perfectly silent electromagnetic gearbox did not sweep away once and for all the crude hotchpotch still used in so-called 'modern' cars. I have often been told of the unreliability of magnetic gearboxes. Although bits of iron whirring around in every direction may possibly seem more reliable than an electrical circuit, hundreds of thousands of electromagnets are functioning all the time in millions of mechanical devices.

The truth lies elsewhere. I have reflected at length on this vexed question of the use of motorcars by drivers who are absolutely incapable of any mechanical intervention. In essence, one is led to the following conclusion: a motor car must above all be constructed by means which are infinitely simple, visible, accessible and comprehensible to the most ignorant, and must on no account be a complex organism whose functioning remains, despite its safety, full of surprises.

Our 12-cylinder and its magnetic circuits, its carburettors and filters, its complex controls, all its meticulously aligned conduits, was much too 'scientific'. The company also suffered from my constant new projects. I alienated the clients. And finally, fashion deserted us too.

One day I overhead a layabout dismissing a magnificent Aérosport parked in the rue de la Paix as 'just another Voisin'. He was absolutely right. It was indeed 'another Voisin', another unusual device, with yet more unfamiliar shapes, another novel display of luxury, another testament to our daily tribulations... Had we disappeared from the limelight for a while, public reaction may perhaps have been more favourable.

The decline put us in an impossible situation. The unproductive elements who had insinuated themselves through every door and by any pretext into my company became ever more numerous. They were friends of friends, relations of our best clients, young people "who liked cars" and went to the pay desk every month, because these weren't hourly paid wage slaves but untouchable salarymen. I was alone in resisting this swarm of locusts, convinced that this unstoppable invasion would be our downfall. I nevertheless had other design projects which I fully was determined to complete before taking what I expected to be my final decisions.

The first *Traction Avants* appeared on the streets of Paris at this stage of our story. Front-wheel drive had two great advantages: firstly, the configuration allowed the centre of gravity to be brought forwards; and secondly, it freed us from the incredible stupidity of having the transmission ahead of the driver with the driven wheels at the rear. This inexplicable arrangement puts formidable constraints on body design. The *Traction* isolated the body itself completely from the power train, allowing major savings of weight and cost (since motor cars are sold by weight).

I began designing what I thought would be my last car - and eight-cylinder comprising two 10CV blocks mounted at 90 degrees on an aluminium crankcase.[9] With thicker inner sleeves, the capacity worked out at 3.2 litres. This engine produced nearly 100bhp at 4,000rpm. The gearbox was electromagnetic, and in order to lengthen the transmission, the driveshafts were mated together at the centre of the Gleason crown wheel.[10]

This car was our first to be built without a differential. We had observed that although the differential is necessary for manoeuvring in tight spaces, it could in fact become a dangerous at high speed. For the initial design, we conceived a differential that would lock centrifugally at around 50kph. This arrangement was abandoned in favour of a fixed transmission. In trials, we found it impossible to identify the reasons for a very marked improvement in roadholding. In a word, I never found out whether this superior handling could be put down to the absence of a differential or to having in the process brought forward the centre of gravity. The body was constructed on the basis of an old 13CV saloon, but as our chassis was only 13cms from the ground, the ensemble was extremely low. The elimination of the differential allowed us to incorporate very large brake drums - uniquely, inboard next to the crown wheel.[11] This arrangement was a revelation, which I applied with total success later on to our microcar. The external appearance was of an extremely lowered 17CV; I shall return later to this prototype that never saw production.

We were at the time being dealt an unending succession of blows from an implacable cartel of competitors, against whom we had few resources with which to defend ourselves.

9) Patents relating to this engine (see 668.043) date from January 1929.

10) See patent 663:965, applied for in November 1928, and 672:321 (March 1929) and 675223 (May 1929).

11) See patent 664:682, which preceded the inboard front brakes of the Cord L29 of the same year.

Having made his fortune in quarrying, the Dutch engineer and wartime RFC volunteer Van Roggen (above, about to contest the Monte Carlo Rally) acquired Imperia and Abadal after the armistice, poaching FN's Chief Engineer Arnold Couchard to design a new slide valve model. The Belgian market being more vulnerable to American imports than its protectionist neighbours, he sought economies of scale as the recession continued to bite by acquiring Métallurgique and Excelsior in 1927 and Nagant the following year. Issy bodied a few six-cylinder 10hp Imperias, one of which sat cuckoo-like on the Voisin stand at the Salon, but there were few takers. Without GV at the helm, there was no one to inspire either the loyalty or the fortitude to put up with the deteriorating conditions with which those who worked at Boulevard Gambetta had to cope. The Voisin company lost its direction and its soul along with its *patron*.

We had for a long time lived on innovation, and innovation was no longer possible. Three of our excellent foremen left Issy-les-Moulineaux. Certain skilled men had become indispensable, because the inadequacy of our equipment meant that constant ingenuity was required. Finally, I myself had had enough of constantly battling, both within the company and without.

I decided to sell my interests in the Voisin company, in which I held more all less all the shares. A Belgian buyer[12] presented himself - an amiable enough person and an astute businessman. Had he possessed the slightest veneer of technical understanding, he could have been a great help to me. Unfortunately, the buyer nursed very high ambitions. He confided to me one day his intention to create a European General Motors, which at the time of our initial discussions consisted of a small Belgian factory manufacturing beastly little wheelbarrows.[13]

The man himself didn't displease me. He was quite young, very active and full of ideas. I transferred my shares to him.[14] He negotiated some fixed term loans which he clearly could not honour and received an injection of capital within a few days, since our technical reputation remained untarnished. This additional capital disappeared into the hands of Belgian incompetents. The businessman's unrepaid loans put the Voisin company into serious difficulties which led eventually to bankruptcy.[15]

12) **Mathieu Van Roggen** *(see opposite)*

13) The Liège-built sleeve-valve 6CV Imperia (larger variants of which were clothed in Voisin bodies at Issy and appeared on the Voisin stand at the 1930 Paris Salon).

14) Van Roggen announced the company's acquisition of the Issy firm at the Imperia AGM on May 2nd 1929, with both GV and Voisin CEO Eugène Mongermon serving on the board of the Société Impéria, and four Imperia directors joining the board of a new holding company created early in 1930, the Société Commerciale des Aéroplanes Voisin.

15) As GV predicted, the new company duly defaulted on its repayments to the Banque Nationale de Crédit, and the Société Commerciale des Aéroplanes G.Voisin was insolvent by the end of 1931; the receivers took over in 1932.

The dramatic red and white C25 Aérodyne made its debut at the 1934 Paris Salon.

Having undergone the experience myself at this time, I advise any business in difficulty to go to the bankruptcy court for this reason: an official receiver is not necessarily an enemy. He has essential advantages over the industrialist, anyway: he has almost discretionary powers, and his remedy for over-staffing is immediate.

When we were obliged to apply for bankruptcy, the Voisin company had the benefit of two men of quality as our official receivers: Messrs Mauger and Héreil.[16] Mauger administered our affairs with punctuality and great skill; as for Héreil, he was not one to trawl snail-like through ledgers at vast expense. A believer in the value of technology, he extricated us from a difficult situation, and his career was later to develop in an unexpected way when he took over as managing director of Sud Aviation, where his energy, confidence and courage led eventually to the Caravelle.

At Issy-les-Moulineaux, I initiated lengthy and ruinously expensive legal proceedings to rid my company of the charlatans who occupied it.[17]

I took a few machines with me to a plot I owned on boulevard Exelmans, where I built a small workshop from which I hoped to plan my return to Issy. Freed from the distractions of running the Voisin company, and with a few resources at my disposal, I rediscovered the

16) An astute official of the Tribunal de Commerce de la Seine, **Georges Héreil** became an aviation industry bankruptcy expert after administering the liquidation of Lioré et Olivier and Dewoitine. The rescue plan he devised was based on Voisin creditors agreeing to a three-year repayment moratorium, during which time it was hoped that sales of Marius Bernard's new 3-litre C23 and C24 models would prove robust enough to put the company on a stable financial footing. They of course did not. Héreil himself went on to take over the newly nationalised SNCASE and became president of the Union Syndicale des Industries Aéronautiques. He went on to head Simca before becoming president of Chrysler International.

17) The bankruptcy of the Société Commerciale des Automobiles G. Voisin was followed by the liquidation of the Société des Aéroplanes Voisin in July 1932. Although GV eventually won the court case and succeeded in regaining control of his company in July the following year, it was saddled with massive debts from the Belgian adventure.

old aviation years, with staff I liked, in a company small enough for me to know all its day-to-day activities.

This pleasant respite from the miseries of commerce and sales should have prompted a rigorous self-assessment. None took place. No longer controlled by extraneous imperatives, my pencil was free to wander at will.

I had brought the 8-cylinder fwd to boulevard Exelmans, as I fully intended to use this new design to make a fresh start in the event of an unhoped-for resurrection of the company. The tests I was able to conduct with this new model taught me nothing.

The Exelmans hideaway was often visited by our old clients and friends, and sometimes by strangers. One day I had occasion to receive a young man who mumbled his name and told me of his experiences with the Voisin company. His underslung V12 had been rammed by a lorry while parked, and the company had refused to undertake the major repairs to a model of which my Belgian successors evidently knew nothing. In the course of our meeting, the man saw my front-drive 8-cylinder. He asked me to sell him our prototype and our negotiations ended up with him offering a ridiculous price for the car (which was of course unique).

I capitulated to this unexpectedly advantageous proposition, and my visitor left the workshop at the wheel. Never again did I see this singular buyer, nor find any trace of the car. It is possible that some resourceful amateur may since have recreated with my front-wheel drive the success of our little 10CV that reigned supreme on the *routes pavées*...

The stupidity of the technicians at the 'General Motors of Europe' was giving André Lefebvre ulcers. One day he came to boulevard Exelmans and confided to me his intentions. Renault had made him a substantial offer, and my spiritual son had come to ask for his freedom. I was only too happy to oblige; two days later he was at Billancourt, where he was promptly emasculated by the incumbents of the technical department.[18]

By chance, I happened to meet André Citroën and brought him up to date with our affairs. I owed this astonishing man a debt of gratitude for having helped us years earlier. On hearing that I had yet again blundered into dealings with insolvent charlatans, Citroën said he was prepared to enter into an agreement between our two companies!

Distraught, I told the man from the Quai de Javel that Lefebvre was in any case with Renault. A week later, dear Lefebvre left Billancourt to take up his post as engineer with Citroën, who knew full well what this enterprising young man was capable of. He knew also of the stultifying effect of organisations that defend their own shortcomings at all costs. Lefebvre was installed in a cubbyhole of his own somewhere in the Quai de Javel factory, and supported by a handful of men; he produced the first Citroën *Traction Avant* in three months. This endeavour had not been opposed internally because Lefebvre had joined the firm in June, and the car had taken shape during the holidays. When 'the opposition' returned to Paris at the end of August, the project was too far advanced to be halted. The prototype was up and running, and all that remained was to demonstrate its qualities.

Many people in the course of the last 20 years have wished to be thought of as the originators of this creation that was to determine the future direction of a great and powerful company. The facts are easy to ascertain, and to verify. André Lefebvre, Voisin engineer for 17 years, was specifically attached to the *Laboratoire* - to research, in other

18) Lefebvre accepted the post with Renault to develop the Reinastella in preference to an offer from Lorraine-Dietrich, and left Issy on April 30th 1931 - almost 15 years to the day after he first joined GV. After a particularly acrimonious row with Louis Renault two unhappy and frustrating years later, he left Billancourt in February 1933 and joined Citroën the following month.

The journalist WF Bradley accompanied the inventor on exhaustive long-distance trials of a C7 chassis equipped with the de Lavaud transmission, concluding that it performed better than the standard car in terms of fuel consumption, hill climbing and general roadability *in extremis*.

words. I had designed, constructed and tested an eight-cylinder Knight sleeve valve front-wheel drive car. Lefebvre had participated in the design and the trials of the prototype. He then left the Voisin company, and on my recommendation joined Citroën, where he constructed the Quai de Javel's first *Traction*, which was successfully produced for 24 years without major modification - a production lifetime unique in the history of the motor car.

One of the *Traction* prototypes was fitted with a De Lavaud gearbox first tried on a Voisin over a two-year period with little success.[19] André Citroën was in financial difficulties. He arranged a presentation of this car, whose innovative nature was intended to persuade a group of financiers to back a rescue plan. The de Lavaud gearbox failed in the course of this demonstration, spilling its innards onto the cobbles of the quay; the bankers made their excuses and left.

Citroën was ill, and this setback discouraged him. Michelin then took the business in hand, and the first action of these enlightened and superbly organised people was to put André Lefebvre's *Traction* into production. The rest is history. No external input was involved in the design and construction of this magnificent car, and André Lefebvre was its sole creator, virtually unique of its type as it was. This is not to say that my spiritual son Lefebvre is the 'inventor' of front-wheel drive - Cugnot's tractor, which can still be seen in the Musée des Arts et Métiers in Paris, was front-wheel drive, and transverse-engined to boot!

---

19) The two units were in fact quite different. Dmitri Sensaud de Lavaud's first infinitely variable automatic transmission was an entirely mechanical swash-plate affair. The initial contract for exclusive rights to its use was drawn up in August 1923 between the Société de Construction des Batignolles and the Voisin company, and over the next five years it was tried on every type of Voisin – a total of nine cars were on test by January 1927. GV personally vetoed its adoption in April 1928. The de Lavaud system later fitted to the *Traction Avant* prototypes was a hydraulic torque converter. Famously unreliable, it was dismissed as "an excellent chip fryer" by André Lefebvre for its propensity to boil its oil on steep ascents, and abandoned in 1935.

The months passed at boulevard Exelmans, where we worked on a great variety projects. At Issy-les-Moulineaux, the legal process took its course. First there were the initial depositions, then the preliminary hearings, followed by the appeal - in a word, everything my adversaries could think up to keep themselves busy there.

This interlude gave me some free time. One day, while heading South for a holiday, Sylvia (whom I saw constantly) decided to buy a house in the country. The Palais Garnier star probably aspired to turreted, steeply pitched roofs and grand formal staircases, and I went with her in search of a suitably remote retreat.

We drove back together towards Paris via the small roads that wind along the left bank of the Saône when, just as we were approaching Tournus, I thought I spotted a shapeless half-ruin the far bank of the river. It was the former home of a ferryman which, having been successively converted into a farm and then a bistro, now lay abandoned. This hovel, overgrown by a mangy vine on which every passing tramp had left evidence of his attentions, was sheltered by ash trees, poplars and century-old elms. The waters of the Saône lapped against its walls. Sylvia was able to buy the property for ten thousand 1925 francs.

As was my wont, I drew up a very precise schedule of the works required, sketched out rough plans and then proceeded to finished drawings just as I had done in my architectural youth. The following year, the woman of my desires was able to move into a comfortable and charmingly attractive house. This retreat had a name. The anglers of the Saône referred to it as *la cadolle,*[20] and there was no point in searching for anything better.

Our romantic pilgrimages to the Midi were to cease, as *La Cadolle* became our home through the Spring and Summer. Once tidied up, the garden became a shady, flower-filled

---

20) Lyonnais *patois* for a garden shed.

bower. The Saône ran languidly beneath the windows of our bedrooms, reflecting the morning sunshine through the slats of the shutters.

Sylvia transferred *La Cadolle* to me in 1955.[21] I hoped to see her again on this property of hers, but she wrote to me that she had 'no wish to revisit the pale shadow of past joys'. I was 80 years old, but she was still beautiful; alas, I had nothing left to give her...

There will be those who say that this is no more than I deserved. To explain all the elements of this very long process here would take time, talent and a very large tome.

My situation was difficult. On the one hand, Esmée awaited me in another place with a tenderness that time cannot diminished. On the other, I was faced with a charming being, but one who was adored, spoiled, constantly wrestling with ambition, passions and possibilities which bore no relation to the miseries of my difficult existence.

We never spoke of our respective situations - indeed, I was careful to steer well clear of the icy terrain on which a single *faux pas* on my part could easily lead me into the abyss.

To cap it all, the positions I had occupied for so long had probably left me with certain undesirable habits, and Sylvia herself had adopted an air of authority that bore no dissent. Her position in Parisian society - which was now foreign to me - took precedence over my company. Perhaps I had become too discreet; discretion never pays. Our relationship suffered as a result. Above all, I was no longer a lover, and could no longer be just a friend.

Becoming like a mere relative of this woman whom I loved, and who had filled me to overflowing with such beautiful memories, seemed to me impossible. Our paths parted; time did its work. Absence was to destroy the romance we had lived so passionately for 20 years.

---

21) GV was still living at *La Cadolle* at the time of writing. He later moved to an old mill at the nearby village of Ozenay, where he spent his last years.

Half a century after it first inspired his pioneering aviation work when he saw it on display at the 1900 *Exposition Universelle*, GV was charged with rebuilding the lightweight steam engine that powered Clément Ader's bat-like *Avion N° 3*.

Chapter XI

In Mâcon, which I visited very often, I undertook the transformation of *L'Angelo* with Esmée, whose courage and spirit remained undiminished.

When the house had been rented out as a farm, the roof space was used to store hay. These were very large areas whose oak floorboards had supported the ancient eaves. I knocked down walls, altered the framework, and patched up nooks and crannies. We put in windows, cemented the gable-ends and levelled the sloping garden. Finally, I installed a workshop in a small outbuilding, and a few months of my life trickled by on the banks of my beloved Saône.

Then a buyer appeared for the *Ariel*,[1] which was moored at Juan-les-Pins. Owning a yacht doesn't mean one is constantly cruising - the boat should be taken out of the water once a year or thereabouts. In those days, this wasn't an easy operation. There are two possible solutions, both of them costly: the first involves dragging the vessel on land by a dangerous trolley too small for the length of hull it supports; the second, and to my mind the only acceptable method (apart from going to the expense of constructing a practicable self-lifting mechanism), is to use a dry dock. Unfortunately, dry docks are semi-official facilities whereby one inevitably has to wait for a batch of smaller vessels scheduled for careening.

---

1) The buyer in question was in fact GV's old friend Henri Kapferer, who often spent the holiday season living on the *Ariel* at Golfe Juan. It must have been a romantic vessel, because it was as a guest of Kapferer's on the *Ariel* in the summer of 1928 that the visionary aerospace pioneer Robert Esnault Pelterie met and proposed to his wife.

Despite its name, the *Espiegle* was in fact a British vessel - a famous one. Built in 1900 and sold by the Royal Navy in 1923, it was a 185' Cadmus class sloop which played a pivotal role in the capture of Basra by the BEF in 1914 and is mentioned several times in Lawrence's *Seven Pillars of Wisdom*.

An attempt to do this at Marseilles had immobilised me for three weeks, and the expense and lost time inconvenienced me. I sold the *Ariel* on excellent terms, so I set out to find a reasonably equipped naval facility along the Côte d'Azur. Thus it was that I came across small and completely abandoned dry dock at Villefranche-sur-Mer.[2] Constructed by the Sardinian navy, it was 66 metres long. The draft was shallow, but could be improved. I asked for and obtained the concession for this dilapidated facility, which I then renovated. I had some workshops built on a quay, and Villefranche harbour later expanded more and more with the development of yachting. Although this activity was not profitable, I had at my disposal a base from which to launch my fantasies.

All I needed was a boat. This was awaiting me at Lyon, on the right bank of the Saône. From a Government sale, it was nothing but a hull - but of a magnificent design. The wreck I was going to buy measured 60 metres, with the dimensions of a veritable floating palace.

The French Navy had commissioned five or six similar vessels a few years earlier, and mine had sailed under the name of *L'Espiègle*, which I had to retain for administrative reasons. I installed my friend Letournel at Lyon, and set about resurrecting my yacht. A year later, we were ready to sail down the Rhône, just as I had with the *Ariel* - but this time, I had two excellent pilots from the HPLM company on board.

The journey was not without its problems, as my vessel had quite a substantial draught and was so high that it only just passed under some bridges. The Service des Ponts et Chaussées were kind enough to help me choose the best day - even the best time - for the purpose, and one bright May morning *L'Espiègle* headed for the Mediterranean.

---

2) GV acquired the Bassin de radoub de Villefranche naval dockyard in 1928. It became the Chantier Naval Voisin.

Although we never actually ran aground, we were within just 20 centimetres of so doing at Montélimar.

The bridge at Livron is a suspension bridge. Having taken a sight line from the poop deck, I was certain of being able to pass beneath when a crowd of onlookers, on seeing this enormous white vessel, ran onto the bridge, flexing it downwards in the process. Bonnerdel, the excellent Rhône tugboat pilot who was directing our perilous journey, had to duck beneath the girders of the bridge; as the superstructure (despite having already been lowered) entered this hornet's nest, we escaped collision with only a few centimetres to spare.

By evening, we were at Saint-Louis-du-Rhône; by the following day we were moored in the port of Villefranche, where *L'Espiègle* was practically the only vessel. My nephews were to succeed me in using this dry dock, and *La Darse* is today busy with vessels of all tonnages.[3]

The career of *L'Espiègle* was to be short-lived. Apart from the couple of cruises I undertook in her, she lay along the quayside at Villefranche. Princely dwelling as it was, I considered my yacht to be just as good as a house.

It was an inconsequential event that made me give up my maritime adventures. Sylvia had bought a 10-metre boat, very agreeably fitted out - but it was at Arcachon. One December, the star asked me if I would be kind enough to take it from Arcachon to Villefranche. Accompanied by a sailor, I left the harbour, sailed along the Atlantic coast and entered the Gironde.

---

3) **Georges** and **Bernard Voisin** took over the Chantier Naval Voisin in 1939. It was requisitioned by the Italian Navy in 1942 and then by the Kriegsmarine 12 months later; after mine damage in 1944, it was recommissioned by the French Navy. After the war, the yard was kept busy as a set for several films, including *Captain Horatio Hornblower RN* in 1949, and *The Adventures of Captain Fabian* with Errol Flynn in '51. It was also in demand for converting redundant UK and US naval vessels (usually for smugglers of tobacco and other black market goods). Once the town's biggest employer, the yard finally closed in 1988.

The canal du Midi took me to the étang de Thau, and thence to Sète. On leaving Sète on the way to Marseille, I ran into an incredibly violent easterly wind. Luckily, we had an excellent engine, but this frighteningly dramatic crossing suddenly struck me as being an absurd indulgence, costly, inappropriate and terribly dangerous. I eventually managed to reach Villefranche after truly Homeric adventures, but this 'trip' cured me once and for all of any appetite for navigation. *L'Espiègle* was sold to some Italians, but it cannot possibly have survived the vicissitudes of 39-45. My maritime career was definitively over.

Back in Paris, my *laboratoire* in boulevard Exelmans awaited me.[4] The Issy-les-Moulineaux court cases, which we absolutely could not afford to lose, dragged on. We had in our little organisation a workshop cart with wheels in a lozenge configuration: the two central wheels supported the load, the front and back wheels coming into play only by gently rocking the ensemble backwards or forwards. This trolley was astonishingly easy to use, and could turn in its own length. But that was not its only advantage - when empty, its weight predominated slightly at the front.

Our small workshop was beneath the relatively high level of boulevard Exelmans, and was connected to street level by a 30-metre concrete slope which was slightly concave for drainage purposes. Unladen, the trolley would track straight down the slope without deviating even slightly to the right or left. With the central hollow of the descent alternately correcting the leading and trailing wheels, its directional stability seemed remarkable.

4) GV's design work from 1932 to 1935 was conducted through (and remunerated by) the Compagnie Hellis, which belonged to Noël Noël's younger brother Maurice, who in the twenties had built and administered the Ateliers de Réparations des Automobiles G. Voisin, and sat on the board of Van Roggen's new Société Commerciale des Aéroplanes Voisin. GV's patents during these years (including the sliding roof of the Aérodyne and the radial-engined lozenge car) were lodged in this name. In part repayment for the financial support Noel provided during this period, GV gave him the 2-door C27 Ski coupé shown at the 1935 Geneva Salon.

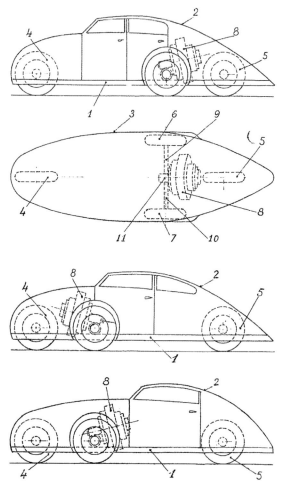

Constructing a simple frame from a few bits of scrap metal, I attached a wheel at each corner in a lozenge configuration with the single leading and trailing wheels steered by a primitive cable arrangement. Having towed the result up to Clamart,[5] I let gravity propel me down the hill.

The device had none of the trolley's automatic self-correction, but I noted that its only steered wheels, front and rear, were mounted on relatively long (and therefore flexible) transverse tubes. Adding crude suspension to the front and rear forks yielded unexpected results: my chassis on casters possessed absolutely extraordinary roadholding qualities, despite the unusually twisty bends in the road.

I began work on a prototype. The lozenge configuration allowed astonishing aerodynamic efficiency to be achieved, but the central position of the engine and driven axle assembly was inimical to any reasonable body design. On moving the driven axle rearwards, I discovered that the exceptional roadholding disappeared.

The reason was clear. Like all wheeled vehicles, a lozenge device has to have its centre of gravity towards the front. On rearranging the masses, I came to a simple conclusion: the engine driving the central axle had to be an exceptionally light unit, so that the weight of the occupants would bring the centre of gravity sufficiently forwards. I therefore envisaged a seven-cylinder radial, which I designed and had built.

My lozenge car would certainly have seen the light of day had I been able to solve the terrible slow running problems in my seven-cylinder sleeve valve radial. Over six long months, I must have constructed twelve or fifteen different types of inlet manifold,

_____

5) A hilly suburb just over a mile from boulevard Exelmans.

Left: Garabedian and GV listen to President Lebrun by the new C30 on the Voisin stand at the 1937 Salon.

Above: Unlike any previous Voisin chassis, the C30's fabricated and heavily flocked floorpan in some ways anticipated the DS Citroën. No more than 60 were built. Although it must have hurt GV's pride to use American power, the Packard six, the Lycoming straight eight and the 3,573cc Graham were considered; the latter was chosen because only Graham would agree to single unit sales. The engine was based on assembled short blocks bought in from Continental, with Graham's own alloy head, carburettor and centrifugal supercharger, which boosted output from 85bhp to 112bhp. The blower was downstream of the carburettor, running at only 5.75 times engine speed. Early examples tended to force petrol into the crankcase, while the vacuum under a trailing throttle would draw oil up into the combustion chamber; thus although the engine was a conventional poppet valve flathead, it was no less prone to smoking than any other Voisin.

heated, cooled, rounded and angular, but I never succeeded in achieving even a moderately acceptable tickover from this otherwise magnificent engine, which yielded 60 horsepower from only 54 kilos. Furthermore, my work was interrupted by a judgement handed down by the Court of Appeal: the occupants of the *Société Voisin* were expelled.[6]

During my absence, the 'European General Motors' had survived off the stocks it had acquired. When the supply of unassembled engines and parts ran out, my successors[7] hit upon a brilliant idea: why bother machining so much metal when it was so easy to buy complete engines and gearboxes from America?

The Graham Paige engine was chosen, and fitted to a few Voisin chassis. The engine was a sorry affair, asthmatic despite its centrifugal supercharger, and equipped with a gearbox quite incapable of withstanding either the demands of our clientèle or our French roads.

When, after 18 months away, I returned to Issy, the factory was empty, its machine tools ruined by incompetents, assemblies broken up or sold for scrap. Although we had won

6) *Les Aéroplanes Gabriel Voisin* had obtained an agreement to reschedule its debt in 1934, whereby the Banque Nationale de Crédit (creditors to the tune of some 14 million francs) took 45% of the equity, with the balance remaining in the hands of GV. Car manufacturing at Issy continued to run at a loss, however, and with little prospect of a revival in the company's fortunes, in 1938 the Bank ceded its holdings to André Bouvier (a former pioneer pilot and director of the Compagnie Française du Caoutchouc) on the basis that the factory's payments would be guaranteed by the sale of its remaining assets.

7) The new company that bore GV's name (and in which he was a shareholder) was the *Société Auxiliare des Automobiles Voisin* (known as SADAV), which was formed in 1937 by the company's former finance director Garabedian after forewarning GV of van Roggen's default. A former professional footballer (and captain of the Voisin factory team), he had joined Voisin as an accountant in 1927 and left in 1935 to set up his own garage in Billancourt. It was to Garabedian that GV had sold the spare parts division and the *Voitures Revisées* company that rebuilt second-hand Voisins, in a desperate (and unsuccessful) attempt to fend off bankruptcy.

all our legal battles, our adversaries were insolvent. I therefore abandoned my plans for resurrecting the company and was prepared to sell once again. I was approached by potential buyers for what remained of the Voisin company, but I had become wary. Only two of their names I recall: Hispano and Gnome et Rhône.

I knew no one at Hispano, but was on friendly terms with the acting head of Gnome et Rhône, Paul-Louis Weyler[8] *(sic)*. He was a man of the world, a businessman, and a good fellow. I knew all about his time in fighter planes, in which he had proved his courage in the 14-18 war. Above all, he was a man of great intelligence.

Our agreement is easy to summarise: in return for Voisin shares, Mr Paul-Louis Weyler accepted the liabilities arising from our previous situation. In addition, he remunerated me sufficiently to obviate financial worries, and I remained president of the Société Voisin.[9]

These arrangements provided the impetus for the old Issy-les-Moulineaux firm to find its former self. The deserted workshops were peopled once again, the equipment was put back in working order, and in a few short weeks the machines were purring away just as they had in the good old days.

---

8) Son of the industrialist, financier and television pioneer Lazare Weiller, **Paul-Louis Weiller** was a prominent society figure for most of his long life. Having graduated as an engineer from the École Centrale, at the age of 20 he was working with Marconi to set up the first transatlantic wireless telegraph link. Four years later in 1917, he led four reconnaissance squadrons, earning the Military Cross and becoming (like GV) an Officer of the Legion of Honour. As secretary general to the Bauer et Marchal investment bank in 1922, he took over as managing director of Gnome et Rhône from the founders, Laurent and Amédée Seguin. Despite having the license to manufacture ABC motorcycles and the Bristol Jupiter 9-cylinder radial, the company had been on the verge of bankruptcy. By the time GV is writing about (1937), Gnome et Rhône was second only to Hispano in the French aero engine market, producing 100 units a week.

9) The transaction took place in April 1937. From then until the outbreak of hostilities, GV's time was divided between overseeing the repair and manufacture of components for Gnome et Rhône aero engines in his capacity as nominal head of the firm (with Marius Bernard overseeing production), collaborating with Garabedian at the SAVA on the manufacture of the C30, and working on experimental projects such as the five-cylinder radial steam tank engine for DEFA (over the winter of 1938/9) with the small *Aéromécanique* team at Boulevard Exelmans.

The *Société des Aéroplanes G. Voisin* (as nothing of this had been altered) entered a period of prosperity. Having abandoned the manufacture of automobiles, we concentrated on making engines. Paul-Louis Weyler assigned me a son-in-law of the poet-ambassador Paul Claudel as director.[10] He was young, energetic and straightforward, and we became friends. I delivered my shares to 150 boulevard Haussmann, where they were filed at the Gnome et Rhône head office. I was as happy as could be. The Voisin company allocated me 500,000 francs a month for research, and I worked in my little *Aéromécanique* workshop in boulevard Exelmans.

An organisation as fertile and intelligent as this couldn't last. In 1939, a certain Hitler unleashed the regrettable chain of events that French people are all too familiar with. Paul-Louis Weyler was a Jew. He hung on until the last minute, but when German troops advanced on Paris, he did what I would have done in his place: he took refuge in Spain or Portugal. But in the haste of his escape, he left the Voisin shares in their pine box locked away in the filing cabinet at the Gnome et Rhône headquarters in boulevard Haussmann. The Voisin factory attempted a poorly planned relocation,[11] which ended in chaos.

I left with the small staff of the *Compagnie Aéromécanique* for Mâcon - to Esmée's. Once the house was put in order, it was possible to accommodate everyone. Then the German army descended as far as the Isère, right across the region in which we had regrouped. The armistice intervened,[12] and the Germans withdrew to the demarcation line at Châlons-sur-Saône. A few days later, I received an official French government telegram inviting me to put the Issy-les-Moulineaux factory back to work.

10) **Jacques-Camille Paris**, who went on to become the architect and first Secretary General of the Council of Europe. Weiller had previously appointed the poet diplomat Claudel to the board of Gnome et Rhône in 1935.

11) To the factories in Lyon and Limoges, in May 1940.

12) June 22nd, 1940.

My director, who was in Brangues[13] along with some of our senior staff, received a similar telegram the same day, and came to fetch me in Mâcon by car. I was in Paris by evening. The staff took their places in the deserted buildings and the factory functioned as normal, machining parts for Gnome et Rhône.

Four years later, I was told that I was guilty of treason. I nevertheless had an official government order in my hands, and the staff, who were paid with exemplary regularity, could put food on the table. There is little point in trying to make sense of it all. The Germans, I found out a little later, had requisitioned Gnome et Rhône as suppliers of civil and military aero engines. They had found the Voisin shares belonging to Paul-Louis Weyler in the cabinet where they were kept, and knowing nothing of our agreement, had concluded that the Voisin company was owned by Gnome et Rhône, with myself remaining in post as president and managing director.

The war years passed. As I have said, we made aero engine parts to order for Gnome et Rhône.[14] The only contact we ever had with the German authorities was very distant, and concerned purely technical matters.

13) The Claudel family chateau at Morestel, on the banks of the Rhône.

14) Mainly crankshafts and timing gears for the BMW 132, an improved version of the Pratt & Whitney Hornet 9-cylinder radial that was the main powerplant for the Junkers Ju52 and Ju86.

Chapter XII

In Mâcon, Esmée and her mother had suffered the repercussions of current events after my return to Paris. Once the armistice was signed, the French authorities immediately made their presence felt. Italy was at war with France. Esmée, although a French national, was born of Italian parents. This shocking revelation became something of a local talking point and gave the Mâcon police an opportunity to exercise their talents. Esmée's Italian mother, who lived with her, was a very elderly widow who wouldn't hurt a fly. She could not understand how after the Italians, as German allies, having stayed at *L'Angelo*, could only a few days later be regarded as the enemy!

The unfortunate woman was summoned, interrogated, detained for re-education, released, re-interrogated and placed at the disposition of a magistrate who never appeared. On being confronted with local Italian workers, she made the mistake of expressing herself in her native tongue. This situation went on for six months before peace and quiet returned to the house, but the two 'undesirable aliens' were confined to their residence as 'suspect persons'.

My position as president of the Société des Aéroplanes G.Voisin gave me access to the necessary permits to travel to Mâcon by rail. I visited often, because the winters were harsh, the Saône freezing over with great ice floes that crashed thunderously against each other, and the complete absence of fuel could only be survived by gathering coppiced timber that a woman on her own could not manage.

During these four years of misery, the circumstances of my two 'exiles' were of the utmost hardship, under constant police surveillance in their hamlet. Unlike on a farm, it was almost

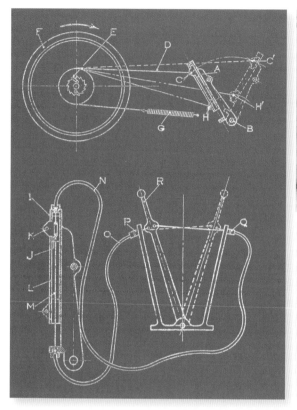

1) Constructed towards the end of 1940 and christened the *Vélogab* by the Aéromécanique team at boulevard Exelmans (including Fernand Viallet, Gabriel Ferreri, Maurice Pain and Henri Bernard), this minimal single-seater bristled with GV's innovations, including this manually variable pedal arrangement with ratchet drive (876.291). The electric motor was fitted in the spring of 1941. Among the many experimental projects GV conducted in secret from the tiny Exelmans *laboratoire* was further development of the ambitious and complex 42-cylinder, 57-litre sleeve valve radial engine first penned in 1938, a novel system of self-correcting seaplane floats and a four-cylinder tractor - even a *cafetière*.

2) A high efficiency 100hp unit with a new type of instant boiler. Its essentials were covered by patents that GV lodged between April and June 1944 (903.657, 905.553 and 905.554).

228

impossible to get food when living in a remote house in the country. Esmée raised rabbits in the garden, but they grew tamer and tamer, taking unbelievable liberties - they became pets, in effect. When the time came for these creatures to be slaughtered, neither of the women of *L'Angelo* could countenance the idea. The same happened with a goat that grew very quickly and virtually took charge of the two 'undesirables'. Taking his place at the table, he would tap his hoof on a plate to demand food. Within a few months, the goat ran freely and it became quite impossible to imagine him on the butcher's block.

There was no question of petrol for cars. A bicycle with wicker baskets was pressed into service to shop for essentials in Mâcon, seven kilometres away. In the winter of 40/41, birds like magpies, crows and jackdaws starved to death in the freezing conditions. Some ash and a few crumbs allowed me to conduct regular massacres, and with as much relish as if they were pheasant, we must have eaten all the local crows and other wild fowl.

In Paris, the petrol shortage immediately made me think in terms of steam or electric propulsion. The first vehicle we built was a very small affair with four bicycle wheels, driven by a system of bottom-hinged pedals acting via cables on a free-wheel mechanism on the rear axle.[1]

The need to transport heavier loads led us to abandon the variable ratio pedal system and fit a bevel gear to the nearside rear wheel, driven by a 13CV Voisin starter motor. With an ordinary car battery on board, the vehicle ran very satisfactorily between boulevard Exelmans and Issy. Eventually I designed a two-cylinder compound steam engine, and 12/17 steel piping allowed us to adapt a boiler. The unit was fired by timber offcuts, of which we had plenty. Our steam van[3] worked extremely well, so much so that I considered a very small production run, but events intervened.

The 1939-45 war was quite unlike what we had known in 1914-18. We of course knew nothing of Nazi crimes, and within our very small circle in Paris, we were completely unaware that any 'secret army' existed. I only knew of the *Maquis* from the events at Saint-Martin-Belle-Roche, and, I have to say, although courageous men constantly risked their lives for the cause, many of the self-styled *maquisards* were nothing but gangs of unscrupulous thugs.

I was in Mâcon when the Allies advanced up the Rhône valley. We had no news whatever of the events that were unfolding in the region, and we were almost taken by surprise when German troops marched northwards through our hamlet.

The Route Nationale 6 was deserted for two days, then a few youngsters armed to the teeth burst into the house. Esmée and her mother were arrested and taken to Mâcon. I took my bicycle and rode to the Préfecture of the Saône et Loire to intercede on their behalf. There, I was faced with not one but two Prefects of the department. Since they were far too busy haranguing each other for me to get any sense out of either of them, I returned to *L'Angelo* - but as I cycled under the railway bridge, I spotted a dozen hooligans looting the house. A neighbour mentioned that people had been looking for me, so I set off on my bike for Paris.

---

3) This was constructed on the chassis of GV's own personal 13CV in 1943; the Edwardian Schneider H bus chassis first acquired by Voisin Frères back in the early aviation days had also been fitted with an experimental steam engine in 1940, as part of a plan to build a giant 30-tonne steam-powered truck.

At Chalon-sur-Saône, I caught up with a convoy of refugees heading in the same direction and slipped into one of the trucks. After two days on the road I was 10 kilometres from Lyon, and eventually found myself back in boulevard Exelmans.

When the Allies finally entered Paris, I witnessed the most disgraceful scenes. At Issy, Marius Bernard and my engineers were arrested, imprisoned and subjected to endless 'trials'.[4] Fortunately, I knew Colonel Tary - a real soldier, not some trumped up, self-styled *résistant*. Taking charge of the matter personally, he set our men free and generally restored order in the locality.

This chaotic state of affairs lasted for a week or so, during which I was summoned to appear before a magistrate in the requisitioned former home of Gustave Eiffel. I had often visited this charming house, and was both saddened and appalled by the filthy disorder to which it had been reduced. The magistrate was an upright and likeable enough fellow who, after formally confirming my identity, informed me that I was charged with "endangering state security" but was free for the time being. I was flabbergasted. After a second summons before another magistrate who appointed chartered accountants, it dawned that I was suspected of embezzling the Voisin company. The accountants came to my home, applied their seals and eventually agreed that my hands were clean.

A third magistrate informed me of their initial findings, and insisted on a second opinion, the results of whose investigations I never learned. Since no one ever formally admitted that there were no grounds for prosecution, I suppose the accusation of endangering state security still stands.

I have experienced many and varied adventures in my time, but I never dreamed the day would dawn when I would be officially deemed a traitor.

---

4) After three months' internment, they were released without charge in 1946.

Chapter XIII

My director disappeared immediately after the liberation. I never knew why he was removed. A young and somewhat impulsive man, he may have been connected with some undesirable political movement.

A few days after his departure, I saw a singularly revolting individual[1] enter the factory on the instructions of some ministry or other. This extraordinary personage went to great and unsuccessful lengths to talk to me in slang. He would speak of 'dosh', 'readies' and 'graft', and announced himself as chief executive of a recently created state organisation: the *Société Nationale d'Étude et de Construction de Moteurs d'Aviation*, or SNECMA.[2] The Voisin company, he added, formed part of this new entity.

During the Liberation I had seen many youngsters from the XVI *arrondissement* acquire really impressive amounts of gold braid from the lowly positions they had occupied in the FFI a few days before; in fact, one of my closest friends promoted himself to the rank of general in only three weeks. Scum as he was, I treated X courteously, but he must have been able to tell that I didn't take him seriously. He returned the following day and with no further comment handed me an equally squalid document, practically obliterated by official stamps.

---

1) **Marcel Weill**, the *polytéchnicien* and communist hardliner appointed to run SNECMA from its formation in August 1945 to March 1948 as part of a purge of all four nationalised aeronautical companies carried out by Politburo member Charles Tillon (one of the troika that ran the French Communist party during the occupation), whom General de Gaulle had appointed to the post of air minister out of political necessity.

2) Honouring commitments made during the resistance years, De Gaulle reluctantly created SNECMA on May 29th, 1945 by nationalising Gnome et Rhône and the other French aero engine manufacturers (including Renault). The new giant's communist management régime came under heavy political criticism throughout the late forties.

I knew from one of my nephews, a St.Cyrien,[1] that General de Gaulle was investigating the whole issue of 'nominations' to public bodies, and would soon put things right. The new 'chief executive' soon disappeared, and the factory was charged with repairing a large number of German engines whose name now escapes me.[2] I was, however, struck by a robotic device that allowed barely qualified personnel to operate complex machines requiring enormous precision.

Although we had excellent managers and an exceptionally skilled workforce of our own, fresh faces appeared in new positions in the company. These recent appointees were apparently famous Resistance fighters, a status that entitled them to important-sounding, handsomely paid jobs. Never in the establishment I had founded so long ago did I see so much ignorance, stupidity, pretension, boorishness, incompetence and naked dishonesty. My poor friend Bernard had to fight night and day to prevent the standards our company stood for from being besmirched by this despicable tide of filth.

This situation had been going on for a couple of months when I finally decided to approach the Air Ministry. I was politely received, and I told them of my grievances about the supernumerary staff imposed on us by some organisation probably attached to the boulevard Victor.[3] Three days later, the members of the Resistance didn't resist for long when they were struck off our payroll. The General proceeded to count the pencils, stamps and stationery, forbade private phone calls and generally put the chaotic situation into some kind of order.

1) **Charles Voisin**, eldest son of GV's sister Aimée, was a graduate of the Ecole Nationale Militaire de Saint-Cyr, the French equivalent of Sandhurst or West Point.

2) BMW 801, 12S, 4L and 6Q engines, as well as Maybach and Waukesha units. The factory was overhauling BMW 132 Z piston engines as late as 1954.

3) Home of the Air Ministry.

His interventions yielded surprisingly positive results; unfortunately this success rather went to his head, and his laudable desire to economise led to his hiring vast numbers of unproductive staff - an expense that soon threatened our finances.

I must have been a nuisance. The liberation was by now in the past, and it was no longer as easy to unseat a chief executive. But he could be emasculated, and in a meeting at 150 boulevard Haussmann,[4] the Scum accused me of having allowed my former director to spend company funds on sport and recreation.

We had indeed built a stadium at Issy, inexpensive in itself but nevertheless requiring proper maintenance. I was dumbfounded by such an accusation, right out of the blue, and had prepared no defence. The Scum simply installed himself in my chief executive's chair, and that was that.

The importance of the share certificates Paul-Louis Weyler had 'forgotten' then came home to me, but I could do nothing. Furthermore, I remained honorary president of the company and kept my salary. In a few minutes, I had been turned into a mere puppet of the Voisin company. Yet again therefore, the most unlikely projects took root at Issy-les-Moulineaux, and I feared the worst.

But the gods were on our side. A little later, under the new government, the situation had become so bad that René Pleven[5] made representations to parliament about the maladministration of our nationalised industries. The Scum disappeared, never to be seen again, and the general, who must have been a crony of his, resigned from the company.

4) SNECMA headquarters

5) A prominent member of the Free French government in exile, **René Pleven** served variously as minister of finance, defence, justice and foreign affairs in successive post-war administrations as well as being elected *Président du Conseil.*

GV had lodged his first patent for the ultra light two-seater *engin démocratique* that was briefly marketed as the *Sulky* in September 1919 (patent 504.416). It featured a simple infinitely variable friction drive operating on the n/s rear wheel. Exhibited at the 1919 Salon and apparently driven by Lefebvre from Paris to Deauville and back, the minimal two-stroke 500cc buckboard (along with the *Motor Fly* motorised bicycle wheel) looked somewhat incongruous beside the large, sybaritic 4-litre cars.

A congenital optimist, I naïvely believed that I would be reinstated as chief executive. Not a bit of it - an odd, colourless individual[6] was appointed, who only graced us with his presence to collect his monthly salary.

We couldn't go on repairing German engines for ever.[7] Before 1939, I had planned to start afresh with our front-wheel drive V8, but unforeseeable circumstances changed my plans when a motorcycle department was attached to the Voisin company in 1946.[8] I was happy to make the acquaintance of the élite group of engineers who ran Gnome et Rhône, and admired the beautiful machines that emerged from their craftsmanlike workshops.

The Gnome et Rhône engines that passed through the hands of my friend Bourguin[9] were particularly powerful - the 125 produced nearly 8bhp, and the 200cc, up to 15bhp. With outputs such as these, it was possible to create very small vehicles capable of carrying two or three people at 60-65kph.

I had prepared the ground for a project of this sort back in 1920-21, and my friend Bugatti also dabbled occasionally in developing similar motorised roller skates.[10]

---

6) **Jean Lepicard**, the administrator who had run Gnome et Rhône from the Liberation in August 1944 to May 1945.

7) Under the aegis of SNECMA, the factory manufactured components for Renault and BMW aero engines, creamery machines and MAP 4-cylinder two-stroke tractor engines as well as repairing Waukesha agricultural engines.

8) Plans for the factory to build a militarised version of the 500cc Gnome motorcycle (updated by Marius Bernard, who was by then reinstated at the factory as well as directing operations at *Aéromécanique*) came to nothing.

9) **Paul Bourguin**, after his successful career as a works rider for Gnome et Rhône between the wars.

10) Perhaps a reference to the 330cc Type 68 prototype of 1940, which was planned for large-scale production at the old La Licorne factory. With its 16-valve supercharged four-cylinder (enlarged to 370cc) revving nearly twice as fast as a T57, Ettore optimistically claimed similar performance to the *grande routière*, with miserly fuel consumption.

Although neither of us found favour with the public with this type of vehicle, we both believed that the day would come when 'very small large cars' would appear on the market.

As to weight, I thought in terms of microcars of less than 150 kilos unladen. I was 65 years old when I penned the first Biscooter designs. Unfortunately, I no longer had the lavish facilities I had at my disposal when I was 30, but was so enthused by the project that I rediscovered some of the creative inspiration that I thought had disappeared once and for all.

The first prototype I constructed in the little boulevard Exelmans workshop hardly needed subsequent modification. The 1945 Biscooter was a side-by-side two-seater powered by a 125cc Gnome & Rhône, driving the front wheels, naturally (*see appendix II*).

With two adults on board and 20 kilos of luggage, the Biscooter weighed 300 kilos. Although not aerodynamically exceptional, it was neither a mechanically undistinguished bubble car nor a large car reduced to a child's scale, and sustained 65kph very easily. I personally often drove one over considerable distances - Paris to Lyon several times at an average of 55kph, for example, matching the speed of much faster cars unable to overtake heavy lorries on long hills with our congested roads. Driving on my own through the bends of le Morvan,[11] I could overtake the lines of bad drivers who choked the road. Thanks to an excellent windscreen and an efficient hood, one was comfortably sheltered from the elements. As to the Biscooter's economy, nothing else even came close.

The testing ended when a new 'president' arrived at the factory - an amiable enough fellow, energetic and with intelligence and vision.[12] He immediately understood the benefits of

11) A mountainous region bordering the Saône-et-Loire.

12) **Henri Desbruères,** who ran SNECMA from 1949 until 1964.

our microcar. When the *Salon du Cycle*[13] opened its doors, the Biscooter was extremely well received by technical correspondents of the motor press, who are often remarkable men. We took 1,430 orders in a few days, accompanied by deposits.

I could see this machine rescuing the old company, and production plans were set in motion. Our engines were perfectly production-ready and easy to manufacture. Henry Potez[14] constructed a very pleasing body for the car and we were just about to begin when the president left the company.

There followed a series of events designed specifically to prevent me from regaining the slightest influence within the Voisin company.[15] In the absence of a chief executive, there appeared a 'director' - a known wrecker, and justly feared as such. Personally, I considered this cretin to be highly dangerous, but with friends in high places, he set about wrecking the world's oldest aeroplane company once and for all.

Convening a board meeting, he stressed the dangers of launching an entirely new product. Sensing that the board was less than receptive to his venomous critique, he changed tack. "If we're going to build a microcar," he declared, "it should be one beside which the present proposal will look like the piffling child's toy that it is."

---

13) The 1950 *Salon du Cycle et de la Moto*. Priced at 150,000 FF, the Biscooter cost nearly 40% less than a 2CV and was small enough to be driven without a licence.

14) An almost exact contemporary of GV's, **Henry Potez** was (along with André Lefebvre and Marcel Dassault) among the first graduates of Sup'Aéro. Having built over 10,000 aircraft under his own name since 1919, he left the company he founded when it was nationalised in 1937. After a damning report revealed the extent of internal disorder and low morale within SNECMA, Potez was appointed special administrator in July 1948. The initial run of 17 Biscooters was manufactured at Argenteuil by the Société des Avions et Moteurs Henry Potez.

15) Having been given one of the Potez pre-production models for evaluation, GV's assistant Maurice Pain later revealed how SNECMA politics conspired against the project to the extent that he was pressured by senior management to report negatively on the car.

Moglia was a French-domiciled Milanese who designed racing engines for Owen Clegg at Darracq before moving to Ballot (where he also contributed the cigar-shaped body of the 1922 Strasbourg GP car), and thence to STD at Suresnes, where we was involved in developing the Sunbeam Super Sports. In 1925, Bugatti turned to Moglia to design the *pur sang* blower. As well as a clutchless hydraulic transmission in 1924, Moglia also penned the Naçional Pescara straight eight displayed on the Voisin stand at the 1930 Salon. For Prince Djellaladin (for whom he had designed the *Djelmo* LSR car driven by Foresti in the twenties, along with an abortive GP car), he conceived a mid-engined streamliner in 1931. Moglia was also responsible for the Hotchkiss H35 tank in the mid-1930s, and was working (also at Issy-les-Moulineaux) on designs for light armoured vehicles during the same period as GV.

Asked to explain what he meant, this technical ignoramus launched into a fiendishly clever tirade that must have made its mark on the board, as the Biscooter project was halted there and then.

This splendid fellow now had the chance to give us the benefit of his talent - and what an absurd result it produced. At the taxpayer's expense, the Cretin came up with a mechanical absurdity, and his 'masterpiece' broke in half during its first tests, hospitalising the two unfortunates who had built the stupid thing. The programme was of course suspended, having cost our company a few million, and all the deposits already taken for my Biscooter were returned.[16] The Cretin remained master of all he surveyed. He had won.

At over 60 years of age, I thought the endless round of work, high hopes, delusions, big projects and swindles was behind me. I looked forward to a carefree life of leisurely reading and study. But the infernal powers had decided otherwise, leading me through purgatory before welcoming me to hell.

A Spanish delegation[17] came to boulevard Exelmans in 1950 to negotiate a licence to manufacture the Biscooter. Its development had been at my own expense, and the patents were in my name.

16) SNECMA's 1951 alternative to GV's design was the work of **Edmond Moglia** *(see opposite)*. It had the same Gnome et Rhône R4, but driving a single rear wheel and suspended by rubber Nieman rings. Fragile and unreliable in trials, the second version shown at the 1952 *Salon* attracted only ten orders, giving management cause to abort the entire microcar project.

17) This meeting took place on January 11th, 1953. Having seen GV's original Biscooter prototype at the 1949/50 Paris Salon, Damián Casanova, a Toulouse-trained engineer, heir to the giant Catalan Farga Casanova ironworks and head of the Autonacional factory, was accompanied by Lorenzo Marco Sarrió, a founding partner of Autonacional, and Benito Jofre of Cadenas BJ.

Clockwise from top: GV with Franco; in one of the prototypes with Casanova in 1953; the flyer for the 1955 model bore the logo of the Voisin dockyard, and the surname of GV's stepfather (presumably for legal reasons); GV in the back of the four-seater; the large oil-cooled cylinder head fitted to both Gnome- and Villiers-engined variants; and the Biscuter factory at Sant Adrià del Besós.

The technical side was represented by a young Spanish engineer called Damien Casanova, who had studied in France and combined all the attributes I value in creative people. A brief conversation was all it took to outline a production programme, and Casanova returned to Barcelona with all the information he needed to construct a lightweight, super-economical vehicle to met the needs of a clientèle who, having been hitherto deprived of their own means of transport, would use it to carry about the most extraordinary loads.

The engine was a 200cc Villiers made under licence in Barcelona, and it struggled to produce 8-10bhp.[18] The Biscooter had a robust front-wheel drive arrangement, and weighed around 200 kilos in road trim.

Disembarking from an ancient DC4 three months after our Paris meeting,[19] I was delighted to find three prototypes waiting for me at the airport. Before long, the factory was up and running and the Biscooter proved a tremendous success.[20] Issy-les-Moulineaux no longer held any charms for me in its guise as a state-owned company, and I made arrangements to move to Spain.[21]

18) The Villiers engine built by Hispano Suiza was the 197cc two-stroke used in many post-war motorcycles, producing 9bhp at 4500rpm and revving easily to 5800rpm thanks to roller bearing mains. In Biscuter guise, it was equipped with a version of the ingenious extra-wide oil-cooled cylinder head that GV had originally designed to augment the air-cooling of the 125cc Gnome & Rhône R4 of the prototype. As neither the French or Spanish variants of the Biscooter had a fan, the excess heat (especially when idling) was dissipated in the three pints of oil sealed in the deeply finned head.

19) GV must be referring to a subsequent meeting after contracts had been signed, because it was in June 1953 that he went to Barcelona to see the prototypes, two of which were exhibited at Barcelona's *Feria de Muestras*.

20) The contract with Autonaçional to build modified Biscooters under licence (as the Biscúter-Voisin, converted to lhd and adapted by Casanova under GV's supervision) was signed in May 1953. The first orders for the Series 100 *zapatilla* were delivered in March 1954, and soon the 220 workers of the Autonacional factory at Sant Adrià del Besós were building 330 a month at a unit price of 28,600 pesetas – a quarter of the price of a contemporary Renault 4CV or Isetta, but still equivalent to three years' average wage. According to René Bellu, some 38,000 Biscúters were sold between 1954 and 1958 (though Kousbroek and Montagu say 'over 20,000').

21) GV lived for part of the year in Spain between 1954 and 1957.

My friend Casanova rented me a house at Castel de Fels for the first year; living alone, the evenings seemed interminably long. Like a new baby born to old parents, my success came too late.

Yet the Biscooter had transformed my life, and I found myself once again dreaming of who knows what optimistic plans. Then I met and absolutely charming young Frenchwoman[22] - a prodigious musician, dazzlingly intelligent, and, not unimportantly, extremely beautiful to boot. Difficult as it was to be attractive at my age, I became friends with this Spanish-speaking compatriot.

I left Barcelona every month to attend Voisin board meetings, and every month I returned to Spain depressed by their utter futility. I became increasingly inclined to the idea of living in Spain permanently. The climate was agreeable and it was a real pleasure to work with the leading lights of Catalan society who surrounded me.

One lonely day I realised with some sadness how often my thoughts turned to Henriette, the musician. I had to extricate myself from a situation whose ridiculousness assumed a disproportionate importance to my eyes. Soon after, I had to go to Madrid for General Franco's visit to the headquarters of Autonacional, our factory in Barcelona. On the evening I arrived in the capital I went to the ballet, where I was astonished to find that the prima ballerina was one of my close friends, Alexandra Danilova.[23] Over supper together later that night, I told her of all my adventures.

22) **Henriette Grellier** (1910-1982), a former ballerina at the Palais Garnier in the 1930s

23) A pioneering Modernist dancer, **Alexandra Danilova** (known as Choura) was the first of Balanchine's muses while still in her teens. In 1924, Diaghilev absorbed her little company into his Ballets Russes, where she remained prima ballerina. With legs so stunning that they apparently prompted standing ovations, she had emigrated to the US with Massine's Ballets Russes de Monte Carlo. Ironically, the production in question was Offenbach's *La Gaieté Parisienne*.

It transpired that Alexandra Danilova knew Henriette. When the time came for us to part company, the *Ballets Russes* star asked me point blank:

"Why don't you marry our mutual friend?"

I explained my doubts and fears, the fact of my advancing years and the inexorable yoke of hideous old age. My arguments were so adroitly parried that I was caught on the hop. Alexandra pressed her case with unshakeable conviction. Within a few days, her tour had moved on to Barcelona.

A little later, Henriette proffered me her hand, and the following month I went to the French Ambassador, who readily agreed to marry us. The Biscooter steadily filled the roads of Spain. I was received approvingly everywhere I went, and had no reason to expect anything untoward.

My second year in Spain was spent in the suburbs of Barcelona in a house bordering on open country, surrounded by a rose garden and neighbours enjoying a modestly frugal life.

Spanish children are educated strictly, the boys by priests and the girls by nuns. Their education is neither free nor compulsory, as it is in France. But in the area where we lived, the benefits of such a system were plain to see. The refinement of the local Spanish children who constantly visited us was astonishing, despite their modest backgrounds. A little four year-old girl who had adopted us was amazed one day to discover the joys of hot water in winter! Tactfully enquiring as to why, we learned from the children that hot water was "too expensive".

Far right: The first deviation from the original Biscuter was the 200-C estate, with steel cab, plywood sides, reverse gear and electric starter.

Near right: The design's minimalist essence was thereafter progressively diluted by the addition of various weighty fibreglass bodies styled like miniature full-size cars - even a mini-Pegaso, the *Pegasino*.

The Biscooter operation was brilliantly managed, and unexpectedly profitable. However, I began to sense a faction of malcontents at the heart of the organisation; people who drove big American cars rather than Biscooters, and who were therefore incapable of appreciating either the benefits or the economy of our little motorised wheelbarrow. This 'opposition' failed to understand that any genuinely original creation evolves slowly, until one fine day a butterfly emerges from the chrysalis. These gentlemen were furthermore blissfully ignorant of anything to do with transport, and it pained them to see our vehicles unembellished by the chrome and superfluous ornament that, in their eyes, a car must have to be worthy of the name.

No customer ever complained about the Biscooter's appearance, but as this same design continues to sell at exorbitant prices in 1962, they must all appreciate its real qualities. Under the strictest secrecy, these gentlemen ordered an intelligent and capable works foreman to turn my purely functional machine into a sumptuous 'Cadillac' *(see opposite)*. The ridiculous bodywork that resulted was a complete disaster, overwhelming the already overstretched 200 cubic centimetres. The factory, hastily restocked for the purpose, collapsed. Damien Casanova resigned as soon as the 'opposition' launched its first offensive. He was of course never replaced, and in this enterprise where I had enjoyed incredible freedom, I was once more duped, swindled and ridiculed.

The passage of time erases disillusion. In 1961, ten years after its launch, Mallorcan roads are full of Biscooters that crafty locals hire out to tourists for 3,000 francs a day. Like the 2CV, the original model survives unmodified, triumphing over the army of imbeciles whom it literally sickened from day one.

I returned to Paris. The company, which had been reduced to selling off its own assets in order to survive, had just sold the boulevard Exelmans property of which I was unfortunately only the co-owner, and the 50 million francs it realised were already absorbed by an organisation irretrievably enmeshed in chicanery, stupidity and ignorance. I took refuge in a little rabbit hutch tucked away in the rue des Pâtures,[24] in the 16th *arrondissement*.

Fortunately, I still had the last vestiges of my loyal team: Henry Bernard, the son of my old friend, and Ferreri,[25] who was an excellent draughtsman as well as a gifted mechanic; and in the workshop, Marceau and Côme, a real professional capable of turning his hand to almost anything: devilishly skilled at working metal, turner, joiner, mason and plumber. Finally, Georges Perrichon. Georges was outstandingly talented. Not only could his hands turn sheet metal into a work of art, but his abilities as a tester were of a very high order indeed. An exceptionally able driver, he could sense the difference between a lack of rigidity and excessive stress, and was the most exacting critic in matters of steering. With men of this calibre, I could do anything.

One morning I received a visit from a young French officer who was a born mechanic.[26]

24) The sale of the Exelmans workshops was prompted by the parent company's objections to the agreement by which Aéromécanique produced the Biscooter in Spain. The payments it was making to the Voisin company (part of which went to meeting the modest salaries of the 10-strong Aéromécanique team) were also suspended. GV and his entourage moved to rue des Pâtures late in 1955, from where two further versions of the Biscooter (with three and four seats respectively) were built. In February 1956, the tiny premises also accommodated the fledgling company of Jean Bertin (of *Aérotrain* fame), to whom GV eventually transferred ownership of Aéromécanique.

25) Addressed affectionately by GV as *Monsieur l'ingénieur,* the self-taught **Gabriel Ferreri** had joined Voisin in 1930 and remained with him until 1958; it was often to Ferreri that the old man turned for corroboration in writing this text.

26) **Captain Viard** of the Direction des Etudes et Fabrications d'Armes (DEFA), the French national defence research and procurement agency. It was Viard who attempted to rescue GV's personal straight-12 Aérosport prototype from the advancing Wehrmacht; although he succeeded in driving it away from boulevard Exelmans, overheating problems prevented him from ever reaching Mâcon, and the car was abandoned en route.

He understood perfectly that engines, of whatever sort, were at the heart of all armaments. Having heard of our tentative 1941 experiments with the steam-powered truck, he had come in his official capacity to ask me to study the feasibility of using steam engines in battle tanks, which I did.

The transmission and drive elements presented no particular problems. The two engines of my tank each drove one track, allowing unprecedented manoeuvrability in every direction. The real difficulties arose with the steam generator, oil-fuelled of course to reduce the risk of fire. It proved impossible to arrive at a reasonable solution that satisfied the young officer. The boiler problem was so central to the overall configuration of the machine that I eventually had to abandon this hugely demanding technical project entirely; only nuclear energy can provide a satisfactory solution. After the steam tank, I was given the brief to develop a parachutable amphibious Jeep-like vehicle by a freshly minted (but also mechanically knowledgeable) lieutenant. The machine I was to design and build had to be able to climb steep slopes and tackle rough terrain with four fully armed men aboard, sustain 70kph across flat country and cross rivers and lakes, all with a maximum weight of 300 kilos.

The design and construction of this unusual vehicle was a brilliant success, much acclaimed by the DEFA. Powered by a Dyna Panhard flat twin - one of the best engines I know - our TEP (Transport Estafette Parachutable) had four-wheel drive and four-wheel steering operated by separate steering wheels for the front and rear. Manoeuvring more nimbly than a moped, it could travel diagonally and turn in virtually its own length. A marine propeller could be engaged when crossing water.

The DEFA representative who worked with us on this project was an unusually intelligent

Above: With all four wheels driven and steered, the amphibious TEP prototype was built in 1952, and bristled with innovative ideas. The Panhard twin was mounted high, and steering, transmission and propeller were actuated by chain.

career officer supported by a team of remarkably competent mechanics and technicians. The TEP was just about the enter production when there was a change of commanding officer in the section concerned. The newcomer of course discarded the efforts of his predecessor and threw himself into developing fancy parachutable vehicles at the taxpayer's expense.

All it takes to understand military air-portables is a careful reading of Cornelius Ryan's *The Longest Day*. The fact is, wars are no longer fought as they were. Parachuting in daylight is today an impractical concept, and all but impossible at night. The only practicable means of aerial transport near front line operations is the helicopter. In Russia today, even prefabricated houses are transported by helicopter; helicopters are capable of evading both visual and radar detection by flying very close to ground level and behind natural obstacles, and they can land in areas completely inaccessible to aeroplanes.

Our TEP was banished indefinitely to a hangar. It was nevertheless a military machine over whose design I had taken infinite pains, having had to construct an armed vehicle within understandably draconian weight limitations that could be folded, adapted to various sizes, shortened or lengthened: a truly acrobatic machine, in other words.

After the TEP and the success of the Biscooter in Spain, I was inundated by propositions. Some evaporated at the very mention of my remuneration; others disappeared in the wake of political upheavals, as happened in Morocco and Argentina.[27]

---

27) Designed from the outset for production with a minimum of machine tools and skilled labour, the C31 ideally suited the requirements of developing countries, but the various proposals came to nothing. Plans for mass-producing the Biscuter in Argentina were scuppered at the last minute by the fall of Perón in 1955.

PLUS DE 10.000 EXEMPLAIRES DE CETTE FORMULE CIRCULENT EN ESPAGN

Above: the Voisin Watani (homeland) of 1956/7, an attractive four speed, four-seater elaboration of the Biscooter with adjustable suspension and rear disc brakes, and proposed for manufacture in Morocco.

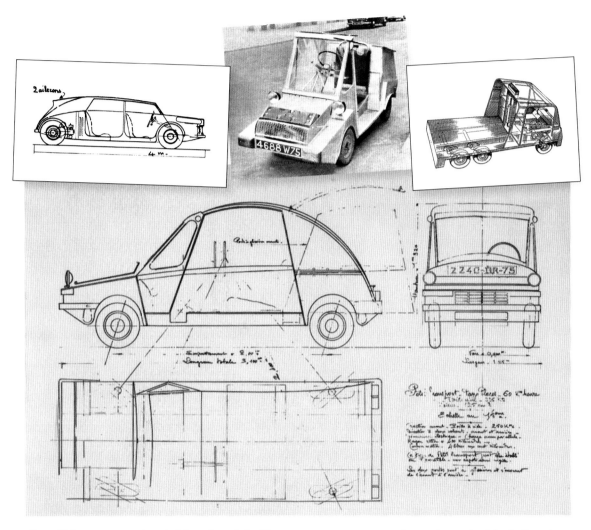

Above: This two-seater closed elaboration of the Biscooter concept was one of several conceived for India and other developing countries, with sliding doors, dual steering and a constant radius sliding roof like the Aérodyne.

Top left: Design study for a low, aerodynamically efficient, medium-sized rear-engined saloon with unusually spacious passenger accommodation.

Top centre: The minimalist 125cc single-seater postal van regarded as too primitive by the *facteurs*.

Top right: Voisin's 200cc six-wheeled fwd light utility appeared on the Gnome et Rhône stand at the 1956 Salon, designed mainly for use in large industrial sites. One was in use until 1977, and survives.

I had dealings with Israel, Ireland and India.[28] I was constantly wrestling with technical projects and documents that were hard to understand and translate - all with no hope of success because the illiterates employed by the French taxpayer who, failing to grasp the difference between export and "stock unsold abroad", gave away such stock to idiots "in order to get business going."

One day in June 1956, the postman of a tiny village in the Ain stopped in front of one of my Biscooters that had seen regular use in the region for several years. He told me that doing his rounds on a moped all the year round made it difficult to guarantee a regular service, what with the accidents, colds, sinusitis and bronchitis that immobilised a proportion of the postal staff every winter.

"Your little car would be the answer," he said. "We'd be on four wheels rather than two, and we'd have some shelter on our rounds. As to running costs, they'd be about the same as a moped."

I constructed a prototype, once again at my own expense, and presented it to the postal service.[29] Their technical department, remarkable engineers who were experimenting with new materials, received me graciously. My machine met their criteria perfectly. Tough criteria they were too, as an engine of no more than 125cc engine was essential because the Post Office could not contemplate anything that would involve the ruinous cost of paying for 100,000 driving licenses.

---

28) The two-door fwd four-seater light car GV designed for the Indian market in 1961 was to have a (presumably BMC-derived) 848cc engine in a duralumin monocoque; 3.64m long and 1.2m wide, it was to have weighed 400kgs ready for the road, with ground clearance that could be raised by 20cms.

29) The 1958 prototype of this ingenious tandem two-seater was also presented for evaluation to the police.

The sole example was therefore put in the hands of a postman in Seine-et-Oise. He was a man who (quite understandably) wanted a Citroën 2CV rather than just something better than his moped. Unfortunately French taxpayers, overburdened as they already are, can't provide every postman a four-seater car to carry around 10 kilos of mail. The Seine-et-Oise postman, of whom I never heard again, rubbished my little car in his detailed report.
No other trial - perhaps in a less wealthy area than the Seine-et-Oise - was ever envisaged. I abandoned my little hobbyhorse.

The small car concept is advancing every day, however. Its birth is laborious and protracted because motorists want "an automobile", that is to say, a cross between a living room and a locomotive. As Pierre Daninos[30] once observed, car-mad people put more vanity into their cars than petrol. The fuel in question, expensive as it is in France, is nevertheless squandered with inexplicable thoughtlessness.

Admittedly, most French attempts at building a small car are resounding failures. The reasons are simple: they are either genuinely original and innovative creations with extravagantly absurd forms of completely unacceptable size and no mechanical integrity; or they are scaled-down large cars, reduced to the dimensions of a silly toy - and even then, buyers are understandably dissatisfied by their biscuit tins on skates, or cabins designed exclusively for the very small monkeys that the manufacturers must assume have serious buying power.

---

30) The journalist, author and humorist **Pierre Daninos** (brother of Jean, the creator of Facel Vega, who worked on the Citroen *Traction* coupé et cabriolet under Lefebvre) was at the height of his fame at the time of writing.

But the small car can't possibly establish itself because our streets and roads and all our provisions for automobiles are defined by grossly outdated assumptions that are extremely difficult to dislodge or replace. So the number of vehicles grows inexorably, congestion becomes an increasingly insoluble (and terrifyingly lethal) problem. Given the impracticality of radically widening the road infrastructure, only one solution remains: dramatically to reduce the external dimensions of our cars.

This doesn't mean that the small car has to be a sardine can devoid of acceleration, good brakes, handling and that aristocrat of all transport requirements: speed. It may be difficult and discouraging (but worthwhile), it may involve educating the buying public and changing drivers' well-known obsession with 'power', but good design can solve the problem of traffic congestion all over the world.

At the Voisin factory in 1957, where I was still 'honorary president' (that is to say, with no say whatsoever in our affairs), disaster followed disaster. The 100 million francs realised by the sale of our stadium disappeared without trace, as had the 50 million raised by selling the boulevard Exelmans site. To crown everything, I lost Marius Bernard. The Voisin company had its final death sentence.[31]

In moments of great anguish, outbursts of unstoppable laughter sometimes break out. Although some of the SNECMA personnel who had infiltrated Issy-les-Moulineaux were unutterable scoundrels, there were also remarkable men who wore themselves out in various thankless and ill-paid tasks. I considered myself a friend of these men, and assume

---

31) Bernard died at the age of 63 on July 16th 1957 while still at the helm of the Société des Aéroplanes Gabriel Voisin.

that in spite of all my insufferable faults, they bore me personal affection. So it was that these friends, these people whom I had always respected and whom I trusted absolutely, were the very ones who administered the *coup de grâce* to the company that bore my name. Individually, none of them would have done me the slightest harm, nor hurt me in any way, but they knew nothing of my past. They were pawns in a fateful game that would lead them to behave in a way that none of my worst enemies had ever done.

On January 13th 1958, we were celebrating the glorious event that gave France a unique place in the history of world aviation - no less than the official beginning of human mastery of the air. It was the 50th anniversary of the first ever closed circuit kilometre flight, undertaken by one of our first clients, Henry Farman, under official observation in a Voisin aeroplane.

The very moment when the troops from the garrison of Paris were honouring our achievements was the moment that my friends from SNECMA chose to close down the Voisin company once and for all,[32] obliterating my name from the very substantial factory I had founded and partly built with my own hands. And as if this wasn't comical enough, the government that had accused me of endangering the security of the state appointed me a Grand Officer of the Legion of Honour.

The day of the anniversary marked the end of my activities. Closing the company removed such means of financial support as I had. A group of friends who were well acquainted with the long history of injustices I had suffered intervened on my behalf. A big-hearted man,[33] whose anonymity I shall respect because I know his feelings on the matter, found a solution to my indigence. The rest isn't worth talking about.

---

32) SNECMA wound up the *Société des Aéroplanes Gabriel Voisin* on January 3rd, ten days before the 50-year celebration.

33) GV's anonymous benefactor was his lifelong friend from the pioneering aviation years, Joseph Frantz, victor of the first air-to-air combat in a Voisin bomber in 1914.

I write these last few lines on the eve of my 82nd birthday. I enjoy the people who surround me, and everything leads me to believe that these feelings are mutual. In winter, I stay with one of my nephews at Villefranche-sur-Mer. For whatever reason, the South of France holds no attraction for me.

In spring, the charming old river I was born beside, and which I still love, opens its arms to me. I often go out for a few hours from the memento-filled home where my life will soon end, returning by the towpath. The walls of a bridge conceal the spectacle that awaits me as I walk southwards under the arch. There before me, perhaps for the last time, the curtain rises on the most beautiful countryside in the world - its immense skies of silver-edged clouds whose iridescence is reflected in an enchanted mirror. A colourful line of fields divides water from sky, and a huddle of majestic poplars shoots forth from a carpet of wild flowers that stretches to the horizon.

As the sun disappears, shepherds blow on their horns to call their flocks. Two different notes can be heard from these primitive instruments, creating unexpected harmonies and rhythms that echo back through the ages. At times I hear the dying cadences of King Mark out hunting;[34] perhaps the ghost of Isolde stalks mysterious clearings in the bird-filled woods that surround me. O Music, lay your cool hands on my eyes and let me see once again the enchanted riverbank where swallows come to skim the clear waters in the light of a summer evening...

---

34) A competent violinist, GV's Wagnerian bent surfaces here, Mark of Cornwall being the narrator in *Tristan und Isolde*.

262

Appendix 1

A critic to whom I submitted this manuscript quite rightly pointed out that although I have drawn attention to some of the constructional errors of others, I have too seldom explained my own ways, good or ill, of redressing these imperfections. The aim of this appendix is therefore to set out for the driver of our so-called 'modern' cars certain solutions which could improve a state of affairs that seems to be getting worse rather than better.

We'll tackle the three most important issues in turn: safety; congestion and weight.

ON SAFETY

We know that many road traffic accidents are caused by the inexperience, incompetence, vanity, bad manners, physical condition and sometimes the youth of the driver, and very often because of the failure to obey the laws that regulate the use of our roads, unusable as they are at high speeds.

But quite apart from this well-known catalogue of exhaustively analysed cases, half as many accidents again - the most dangerous of all - are reported in terms such as this:

"According to eyewitnesses, Mr.X was driving at more than 100kph along road X in free-flowing traffic when his car suddenly skidded out of control, swerving violently before crashing into one of the trees that lined the road. The car was in perfect mechanical condition, the tyres were practically new and Mr.X was a good driver. The cause of the accident is difficult to determine; Mr.X probably lost control of his car after succumbing to some physical illness."

One such 'illness' is perfectly possible - even two. But not the ten, twenty, one hundred thousand illnesses that are advanced to explain this very common and lethally dangerous occurrence. Fatal accidents of this particular type take place on straight, empty, well-surfaced roads. They are surrounded by a complex conspiracy of silence that extends from buying off witnesses to complicated agreements with insurance companies, because any increase in premium category is a grave indictment of the model concerned.

Even the state finds it difficult to intervene in these criminal goings-on. The motor industry is such an economically productive fiefdom that there can be no question of worrying the consumer in any way - the one who pays 1,000 old francs to the Treasury on every 20 litres of petrol, in a highly remunerative tax that's astonishingly easy to collect.

The unknown or little known factors involved in the classic 'straight empty road' accident are inherent defects of the car itself. They are not of course intentional, nor would they be tolerated by manufacturers. The defects, which account for some four thousand deaths every year in France alone, are probably the result of an alarming degree of general ignorance which I shall try and explain in non-technical terms.

Here is a theorem of sorts, which must understood to begin with: *any wheeled land vehicle (irrespective of whether it has two, three, four, six or twenty wheels) whose construction disregards certain principles of 'centring' is subject to forces and physical laws that are generally poorly understood, or not understood at all. Though theoretically complicated, these essential construction principles are relatively easy to determine by practical experiment. Such experiments confirm that at any point in the direction of travel, the apparent stability of the vehicle can vanish surprisingly quickly, causing it to follow inherently unpredictable trajectories that often result in accidents whose severity increases in direct proportion to speed.*

As I say, this is not the place for a technical and scientific explanation of this phenomenon, which would in any case be of questionable use and heavy going for the reader. We shall instead examine the question of 'centring' by means of practical experiment, which though imprecise, is sufficient to demonstrate the point.

Motor cars can be classified into any number of different categories, but for the present purpose let us think in terms of two very distinct types: road cars and racing cars. The latter are constructed for use by professional drivers with a rare combination of talents that include lightning reflexes and the sense of balance of a high wire performer.

I draw my reader's attention to a case in point. There are many excellent and highly skilled drivers with an exceptional aptitude for safe driving. However, I can assure these experienced drivers that there is no comparison whatever between their evident dexterity and the truly monstrous talents of a great professional racing driver.

A race of two to five hundred kilometres between more or less equal machines is won by increments measured in hundredths of a second, and instant manoeuvres of incredible precision take place in these hundredths of a second. Such manoeuvres are only possible with cars whose horizontal equilibrium is low enough to allow the driver to execute violent changes of direction, such as for hairpin bends, as easily as negotiating regular curves, and can only be achieved in the best possible time by machines that bear no resemblance to ordinary touring cars.

A racing car of 1962 has to be constructed so that as much of the mass as possible is concentrated at a point more or less midway between the wheels so as to minimise the transverse inertia of the assemblies at the front and rear. Making allowances for

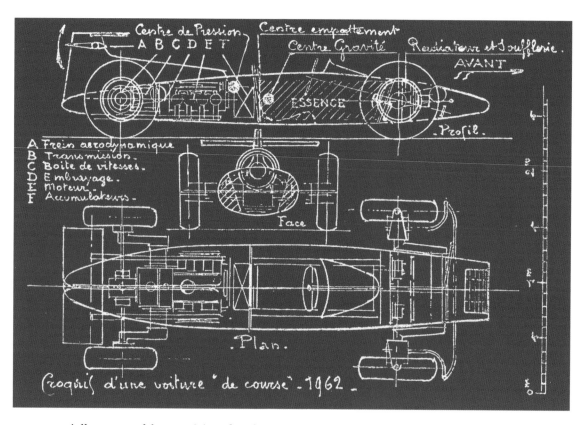

Centre de Pression · Centre empattement
A B C D E F · Centre Gravité · Radiateur et Soufflerie.
AVANT
ESSENCE
Profil.

A Frein aerodynamique
B Transmission.
C Boite de vitesses.
D Embrayage.
E Moteur.
F Accumulateurs.

Face

.Plan.

Croquis d'une voiture "de course" - 1962 -

commercially acceptable provision for the occupants and their often voluminous baggage simply doesn't enter into the equation.

We can conclude that the driver, the engine and its ancillaries, the fuel tank, batteries and so on should ideally be grouped into a compact mass whose centre of gravity coincides as far as possible with that of the rest of the chassis. All this without forgetting that the centre of gravity of the ensemble is always TOO HIGH off the ground, and crucially, that the centres of lateral aerodynamic pressure must at all costs lie behind the centre of gravity - a little-known factor that assures impeccable handling. Ferrari and Lotus racing cars adopted this basic layout some time ago. The racing car outlined above has nothing in common with a road car, as you can see.

Car-mad Frenchmen, who apparently "would rather lend their wife than their car", are divided into two camps: those convinced of the benefits of engines in the front, and those who favour rear engines. A good friend whom I met one June day in 1960 broached the subject thus:

"You know," he said with a twinkle in his eye, "Renault is abandoning rear engines in favour of front-engined front-wheel drive in 1961?"

"You also have to bear in mind," I replied, "that Simca is putting the finishing touches to a new rear engined model."

Valid as the argument seemed, my friend drew a curious conclusion. "Don't be a smart alec. Renault is abandoning the rear-engine layout having built at least a million of them. Either Renault made a gross error in building all those rear-engined cars, or they're now about to make the mistake of making a million front-wheel drives..."

I had neither the time nor the pencil and paper to show this good fellow that there were no cars with everything at either the front or the rear, but, much more simply, some with their centre of gravity behind the centres of aerodynamic pressure, and others in front - the latter being automatically endowed with inherent horizontal stability. And although it is easier to construct a front-engined car with these characteristics, it is by no means impossible to build rear-engined ones with the same advantages.

My friend would hear none of it. He played his trump card: "So why are they now making rear-engined racing cars?"

There was no point in explaining to my 'everything up front' exponent that modern racing cars didn't have rear engines in the same way a Renault Dauphine, but placed the power unit ahead of the rear wheels for the reasons given above. My friend had unfortunately muddled up virtually every law of dynamic equilibrium. For him, the driver either had to have the engine ahead of his feet, driving the front wheels, or behind his back driving the rear wheels - a false dichotomy that I have tried to expose in the following pages.

Whether the engine is at the front or the rear, above or below, only three things matter in the design of a car:

1. That the centre of gravity is ahead of the halfway point of the wheelbase.

2. That the centre of gravity is ahead of the centre of pressure.

3. That the centre of gravity is always too high in relation to the ground.

❖

Consider the problem of touring cars.

When you skim a flat pebble across calm water, it leaps across the surface in a series of ricochets. These provide a surprisingly good analogy for the suspension movements that occur in a road car driving at speed along a reasonably well-surfaced road. Repeat this simple experiment and you will observe that even though your pebble is spinning, it traces a perfectly even line across the surface of the water.

This line is traced by a particular point on the pebble: its centre of gravity, which for the sake of this crude demonstration is near the middle of the pebble. You can easily deduce from this test that despite the very low speed and light weight of your projectile, it can only change the direction of its trajectory to the right or left with the greatest difficulty.

A motor car, whether pulled or pushed along, whatever the position of its engine (front, rear, above, below, vertical or horizontal), irrespective of its power, make, price, number of cylinders or means of transmission, can be made to see-saw across a transverse axis, just as any object of whatever shape can be balanced across a ruler, a pencil or a baguette.

By placing the object vertically on the pencil, it finds itself at a given moment in equilibrium on the pencil, with its centre of gravity high or low in relation to the pencil. But with a motor car, this point is where the vehicle is in perfect balance, and IT IS AROUND THIS POINT, and the path it traces above the ground, through space, in a trajectory that becomes increasingly rigid in relation to speed, that ALL THE MOVEMENTS OF THE CAR take place.

Production cars of 1962 are all pretty similar in terms of their steering arrangements. Their horizontal displacement from right to left or from left to right is occasioned by mechanically inclining the two front wheels. The rear wheels are designed to remain parallel to the vehicle's longitudinal axis. Any change of direction can therefore only be obtained by modifying the trajectory defined by the vehicle's centre of gravity.

What is certain is that this manoeuvre has as its only point of contact with the ground the front wheels which, when mechanically inclined under the driver's control, act on the back wheels to deviate the trajectory of the centre of gravity, situated above the ground somewhere between the front and rear axles.

If, as a result of undertaking the desired manoeuvre at excessive speed, the centre of gravity is unable to be deviated sufficiently from its forward trajectory, the wheel or wheels with the lightest load or the least grip on the road surface lose adhesion, the vehicle is displaced sideways across the road and, complicated by a number of secondary factors, an accident becomes virtually inevitable.

FOR THE SAME SPEED AND FOR THE SAME VEHICLE WEIGHT, it is clear that if the centre of gravity is near the front wheels, the further forward the centre of gravity, the greater the resistance the front wheels encounter when changing direction. But it is equally clear that the further forward the centre of gravity, the greater the vehicle's inherent stability in a straight line. Conversely, the closer the centre of gravity to rear wheels, the easier the deviation manoeuvre becomes, because the leverage of the steered front end is proportionally greater. The disadvantage of this arrangement is that the car loses its 'automatic' straight-line stability, thereby necessitating constant corrections from the driver.

It is a simple matter to demonstrate these elementary truths. Take a box of matches. Empty the contents and stick the match drawer to the outer case to obtain a rigid hollow body. Trace a line along the length of the box on one of its sides, and divide it into four more or less equal parts. Pierce a match-sized hole a quarter of the way along the box and glue in a match so that it protrudes from one side of the box. Take a piece of fine string or cotton about 60 centimetres long and make a loop at one end. Place the matchbox on some piece of furniture or other, or any smooth uncarpeted surface. Tie the loop around the match protruding from the upper side of the box, and pull it neither too fast nor too slowly in a rectilinear direction. The thread should pull on the match a little higher than the box so as not to impair the latter's freedom of movement.

Your matchbox represents a car. The presence or absence of wheels is immaterial to the demonstration. The match is placed at approximately the centre of gravity of the two cars you are about to test in succession. According to whether your matchstick is towards the front or the rear of the direction of tractive effort, you find that the 'car' follows the thread easily when the centre of gravity represented by the match is at the front of the system – or IT TURNS UPON ITSELF when the centre of gravity represented by the match is at the rear. Crude as it is, the experiment you have conducted is an effective demonstration.

The centre of gravity of a laden touring car should ideally be towards the front wheels.[1] We can now see how it is possible to use a car whose centre of gravity is towards the rear, and which, as we have seen, is inherently unstable in motion and consequently dangerous.

Let us turn once again to our matchbox, with the centre of gravity (that is to say, the match) away from the direction of pull exerted by the thread. When you pull on the thread, the car will 'skid' right or left; continuing to pull, straighten the matchbox with your free hand. You may then be able to advance the matchbox a little way before it slides off course again; you will have then experimentally verified the behaviour of a vehicle 'centred' towards the rear.

The driver, whose concentration has to be unfailingly continuous at high speed, executes the function of your manual corrections via the steering wheel, constantly correcting the car right or left, and provided the surface is sufficiently grippy and the tyre tread has sufficient lateral purchase on the road, he can drive his 'unstable' car for 20 years without anything untoward happening.

Millions of two-wheelers, which are by far the most dangerous means of transport of all (accounting for 55% of all accidents), owe their equilibrium to the reflex attentions of

---

1) In the original text, GV refers the reader at this point to *L'Aventure Automobile* by the pre-eminent exponent of front wheel drive in the vintage years, JA Grégoire (pp 52-114 in the original Flammarion edition). The last thing GV ever wrote for publication was the preface to the same author's *50 Ans de l'Automobile* in 1973.

the rider, and two billion human beings walk and run on two legs. But this state of affairs lasts until the first puddle for two-wheelers, or for human beings, the first banana skin, provokes a skid – that is to say, an uncontrolled movement faster than the rider or the pedestrian's reflexes, so fast that correction is no longer possible and the vehicle veers out of control into whatever obstacle lies in its path.

In summary, while it is possible to accommodate vehicles whose centre of gravity is not forwards, equilibrium and safety unfortunately depend on other conditions, of which one – the height of the centre of gravity – is of capital importance in the sense that ALL CURRENT TOURING CARS have their centre of gravity too high in relation to the road. This vice is the main cause of often-fatal roll accidents.

The third crisis of automobile design in general, which lies at the root of so-called 'accidents' occurring on straight, empty roads, is the lack of attention to aerodynamic 'centring'. A car driving in calm conditions at 120kph creates a 120kph draught around itself – the equivalent of a very respectable gale. But if this car is travelling into a 30kph headwind (little more than a breeze), it moves through a 150kph draught.

A hurricane, in other words – and a veritable scourge. Trees are uprooted, roofs lifted away, chimneys toppled, with a rising toll of deaths and injuries from flying detritus borne by hurricane force winds, press reports of natural catastrophe and long faces all round. However, when a driver puts his foot to the floor on a downhill stretch to hit 130kph on the clock in some car or other (which, in a light 30kph headwind, generates an air current of 160kph), the passengers spare not a moment's thought for what would happen if this monstrous force and its potentially tragic consequences for some reason were to strike the car at a more acute sideways angle rather than head on.

There is nevertheless no mystery as to the result: blown violently sideways by this tornado, the car rolls without any possibility of evasive action on the part of the driver.

THIS DRAMATIC EVENTUALITY POSES A CONSTANT THREAT TO THE OCCUPANTS OF 'SPORTS CARS' WHOSE CENTRE OF AERODYNAMIC PRESSURE LIES AHEAD OF THE CENTRE OF GRAVITY.

Given a grippy surface and tyres in perfect condition, drivers of fast cars can, with great skill and excellent reflexes, maintain the vehicles they steer in a state of unstable equilibrium. But if the road is slippery, or the tyres lose adhesion, or they encounter a side wind of more than 40kph, an accident will almost always ensue. The car skids, travelling at an acute angle to the air. Considerable aerodynamic pressure is exerted on the side of the car, and nothing can prevent the inevitable accident, because tyre grip can never overcome the force of a 180kph wind.

The accident is comparable to those that can afflict poorly 'centred' aircraft, which can stall or spiral downwards out of control towards the earth, with no possible corrective manoeuvre. In a word, a car's aerodynamic accident is that of a bad aeroplane except for the fact that the stages involved take place horizontally. To travel safely, one must therefore be aware of the centre of aerodynamic pressure of the car one drives.

Here is an inexpensive and acceptably accurate alternative to testing a scale models in a wind tunnel for determining a car's centre of aerodynamic pressure. To build the 'seesaw', you need lengthwise access to an area 10 metres long by 3 metres wide and to buy or hire two 4-metre lengths and one 3-metre length of 22mm x 75mm pine plank.

Grind two sticks of chalk in a jam jar of water so as to obtain a thick white paste that can be easily removed from the car's paintwork. Get a cheap flat paint brush 30mm wide, and then prepare the car as if you were going on holiday – that is to say, with a full tank, tools, spare wheel, driver and passengers. Put the equivalent of 150 kilos in the boot, if this is at the rear.

Now present the laden car in front of the two 4-metre pine planks, spaced apart to fit the car's track, and drive slowly onto the seesaw under the guidance of a third party. Don't worry about creaking or cracking noises from the wood. Advance very gradually in first gear, slipping the clutch, which you release as soon as the car is in perfect balance, with the long planks in the horizontal position supported by the transverse 3-metre fulcrum.

After applying the handbrake and stopping the engine, get out of the car without worrying about any effect the removal of your weight may have on the balance of the car. Then, on one side of the body, paint a vertical line upwards from the fulcrum with your brush of chalk solution. Your car's centre of gravity when laden is along this vertical white line. This completes the first part of the operation.

Now remove the car from the driveway in which you may have constructed the seesaw to the nearest road and take a photograph of it in profile from a distance of about 10 metres at 90 degrees from the vertical white line painted on the car.

Make two 13cm x 18cm enlargements of this photograph to create two identical images, each occupying the full length of the paper. Take one of these enlargements and carefully cut around the profile view of your car. Place this cut-out on the edge of a school ruler to find its balancing point, where you then draw a vertical blue line. This blue line, which approximates to the centre of pressure, is unlikely to cover the white line you painted when the car was balanced on the pine planks. Remember, your centre of aerodynamic pressure is the blue line. One the other photograph of your car with the chalk line, draw over the white line from top to bottom in red.

Place the cut-out over the other profile photograph so that it is exactly superimposed, wheel for wheel. If your blue line (the line of your car's aerodynamic pressure) is AHEAD of your red line (the line of your centre of gravity), your car is VERY DANGEROUS.

In order to use it safely, taking into account all the risks, it is essential to drive with the rear boot completely empty, a precaution that nevertheless only attenuates the problem. If on the other hand your blue line is behind your red line, thank St Christopher and go on your way reassured, which is not to say you are at liberty to take risks…

This is of course a primitive exploration of a question that cannot properly be discussed in a few moments.

During the winter of 1960-61, in the wake of a chemical experiment designed to reduce the persistent smog that paralysed air traffic at Orly, the condensate gave rise to a layer of frost over not only the runways but also the surrounding roads. The region experienced a hundred or so accidents involving all types of cars in a very short time. But not a single accident or landing incident occurred on the runways, with intercontinental jets weighing some hundred thousand kilos landing at speeds in excess of 200kph with frozen brakes and entirely smooth tyres.

The reason for this 'safety' is simple. The centre of aerodynamic pressure in all aircraft is very considerably aft of the centre of gravity, and this is why not a single aeroplane experienced the slightest skid, even on runways like skating rinks.

ON TRAFFIC

When George Stephenson evolved the steam locomotive, whose fundamentals have remained essentially unaltered since 1820, he had the distinction of conceiving an indisputably original creation. But it is not in this endeavour that he revealed the full extent of his genius. This prodigious talent allowed him in effect to foresee that the locomotive, deprived as it was of what today we call a gearbox, could only be used on more or less flat terrain and could only deviate from the straight on very large radius curves.

George Stephenson had tremendous courage, because he imposed a ruinously expensive programme of works on private companies whose boards were incapable of comprehending the reasoning of this Englishman who only learned to write in order to sign his own marriage certificate. Stephenson's railway sliced through hills in cuttings, crossed mountains through tunnels, strode across valleys on vast viaducts, and this achievement was so brilliant that a century later, Stephenson's railroad was being used for transport which bore no relation in terms of either its weight or speed on the requirements of 1860.

The automobile never had its Stephenson. The road network of France dates back to Chilpéric,[2] and transport on the roads of the idle monarchy was only possible thanks to animal traction. In the era of horse-drawn carriages, it was already possible to change speed, albeit in a simplified manner. At the bottom of a long hill, the traveller used other horses to reinforce his own. But none of the innumerable ministers who succeeded each other for 300 years ever supposed for one minute that a combination of man and wheelbarrow would definitively replace the stable of reserve horses to the benefit of all.

---

2) Echoes of Wagner again. Chilpéric the 1st was the cruellest of France's sixth century Merovingian monarchs; his mention in this context presumably stems from his Visigoth sister-in-law Brünnhilde, whose memory lives on in a number of ancient Roman roads known as the *Chaussées de Brunehaut.*

When the horseless carriage made its appearance, the first examples were the products of intelligent craftsmen, not one of whom had the breadth of vision or intellectual capacity to create a road network in any way comparable to the iron road Stephenson had imagined. Roads remained more or less as they were, an impossibly labyrinthine matrix of tracks doggedly climbing every rise in the land and descending the other side on slopes suitable only for mules and liberally sprinkled with hairpin bends.

The result of this indigence was an incredible burgeoning of pitiful mechanisms for steering horseless carriages, for stopping them by some other means than making the animal strain backwards and starting them without the use of a whip – everything, in other words, that this new form of transport required in the absence of straight, flat roads.

The ingenuity of our pioneers discovered clumsy solutions to these challenges, to which people necessarily adapted themselves. The roads were peppered with obstacles. The pneumatic tyre was invented to allow us to travel on surfaces that bore no comparison to the smoothness of rails. The pioneering artisans of the motorcar drew on the example of carriage shafts to devise their steering mechanisms.

Automobile traffic is in other words chaotic in every way, and if it is becoming more and more deadly, it is because these first craftsmen, widely dispersed as they were, adapted their machines to existing roads rather than uniting their efforts to adapt roads to the newborn mechanical devices they created. Readers who accuse me of being paradoxical will allow me to observe that with the rubber of today's tyres, it would be possible to build cushioned roads that would, with unimaginable luxury, obviate this well-known danger.

At certain times of the year, all of France is faced with a growing and disturbingly pressing problem: the congestion of our main roads, which are virtually the only ones usable.

With the number of vehicles in circulation increasing every day, the situation is becoming impossible. Whatever the solution envisaged, the nation does not have the economic resources to fund the infrastructure the transport industry requires. Our proposed motorways are nothing but improvements to the road network of Pépin le Bref.[3] Their dimensions are absurd, and they will be congested as soon as they open.

It is however possible to envisage workable compromises. Night driving could be massively improved by resolving the problem of blinding headlights. For this curse to be sensibly dealt with, it would for example suffice to equip our motorways, pitiful as they are, with two-metre high shrubbery on the central reservation between the two lanes.

But it seems that such a simple method of easing traffic problems will not be implemented. (Spain, which has no great financial resources, has put this shrubbery idea into practice on the road from Barcelona to the airport. Spectacular as it is, the result is ignored.)

Another straightforward initiative is not beyond the imaginings of a simpleton: making smaller cars.

A senior civil servant to whom I once took the liberty of suggesting such a solution to this apparently insoluble problem replied very politely that he had "no power to influence manufacturers' design departments." Enough said…

Nevertheless, had I been able to present a serious plan, I would perhaps have been listened to. Here therefore is what might well be envisaged as a strategy for resolving the congestion problem.

---

3) Charlemagne's father Pépin III ruled the Franks from 751 to 768.

Cars in France are taxed on their capacity, that is to say, their cylinder size. In dreaming up this formula, it never occurred to the fiscal authorities that a 1500cc engine can develop anything from 10 to 150 horsepower. Capacity-based taxation is therefore outdated, and a self-evident idiocy.

In order to generate the funds to build new infrastructure, the French government has introduced unpopular levies such as the 'tax disc' and excessive taxation on petrol. Admittedly, it is difficult for the state to impose size restrictions upon manufacturers (even supposing that our government could find men capable of debating the issue, pencil in hand).

Having said which, I suggest: 1, abolishing capacity-based taxation; 2, abolishing the 'tax disc'; 3, getting rid of all non-essential ancillary taxation.

These taxes would be replaced by a levy on the area the vehicle occupies. This measure, which could not be unpopular, would compel every research department in France to investigate intelligent ways of reducing the external dimensions of their products, because the external size of our car bodies, grotesque as they are with their ridiculously thick doors, must never be confused with the internal dimensions which are the only important consideration.

People will say that the attempts made in France to build genuinely small cars have been disastrous. My reply is simple: it's not a question of repeating versions of today's biscuit tins on wheels or reducing big cars to a scale suitable for monkeys, with the ensemble in either case powered by a confection of disgracefully impoverished mechanical systems.

A 'truly small car' must have standard internal accommodation. But this new type of car won't have doors that occupy 40 centimetres of the vehicle's total width, nor empty under-bonnet space, nor ridiculously exaggerated luggage areas.

A four-seater car can easily be 1.205 metres in overall width and 3 metres in overall length. The design and construction of such a car is no easy task, but it is quite possible, and to achieve absolute comfort to boot. I advise disbelievers to study in detail the doors of a 2CV Citroën.

This 1.205-metre wide, 3-metre long four-seater occupies an area of 3.6m^2, compared to the 1.4m^2 or so of a conventional moped, which carries two people in tandem so unsafely as to be not worth discussing.

A design sketch for a small four-seater car appears in the next section.

❖

ON WEIGHT

For thousands of years, even the most technically illiterate have understood that weight is the N$^{o.}$1 enemy when it comes to matters of transport. Yet no automobile technician worthy of the name has ever proposed an original design that would massively reduce the unacceptably excessive weight of our so-called 'touring' cars.

There nevertheless exists a shining example of technical brilliance in this field: the racing bicycle. Such a marvel can complete the Tour de France at an average of 45kph, descending Alpine cols at 60kph, while tipping the scales at only seven kilos. Assuming a 70kg rider, it therefore carries no less than 10 times its own weight.

By comparison, so-called modern cars have an average unladen weight of around 1,000 kilos in order to transport some 250 kilos of passengers. In other words, a four-seater touring car requires 250 kilos of ironmongery to carry a load of 70 kilos – no less than THIRTY FIVE TIMES HEAVIER than a racing bicycle.

How is it that customers tolerate such a product? Because cars are sold at 1000 old francs a kilo, remember, so a one-tonne car costs a million old francs! A four-seater touring car unladen but complete with spare wheel, should weigh no more than 400 kilos.

Appendix 11

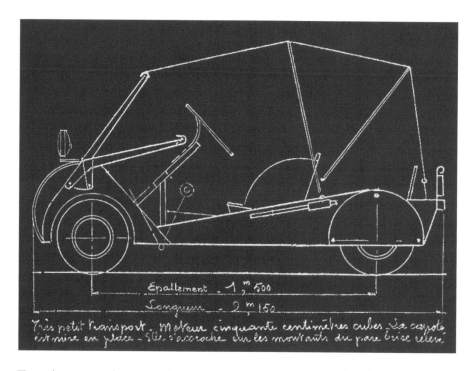

A million French men and women have no access to a very small vehicle capable in all weathers, in the safe and sheltered conditions that only a four-wheeler can provide, of outperforming or even replacing one of the most dangerous forms of transport of all, the two-wheeler.

The purpose of such a very small car is to carry small loads over short distances, to transport the household shopping or to ferry around a child too young to be left alone at home.

A 50cc engine is what we suggest, which is both familiar to users and successful in France because its toy-like capacity is below the road tax threshold, requires no driving license and escapes the tax recently levied on 125cc machines in a bid to kill the moped, which will soon disappear as the scooter has done.

The best makes of touring car are sold second-hand in France at prices one would think affordable for people of modest means. But if the purchase price of such a vehicle is almost derisory, the maintenance and running costs are prohibitive enough to make it an unacceptable solution.

Secondly, the very small car often has to be parked in a very restricted space with poor access that cannot be inexpensively improved.

In this design, the windscreen can be inclined downwards to reduce the wind resistance of a machine whose form is by its very nature difficult to streamline. On the flat, the vehicle can sustain 25 or 30kph. The wheels are scooter wheels, and a very low-geared system of pedals allows small distances to be covered without the aid of the engine at all.

It weighs 70 kilos unladen but with spare wheel, and even if manufactured on a cottage industry scale, should carry a price tag of around 700 new francs.

But to understand the true value of such a machine, it must be remembered that a Cadillac – even a free one – is not an acceptable form of transport for someone who has to make do, and that our proposal offers innumerable advantages over the best two-wheeler imaginable.

❖

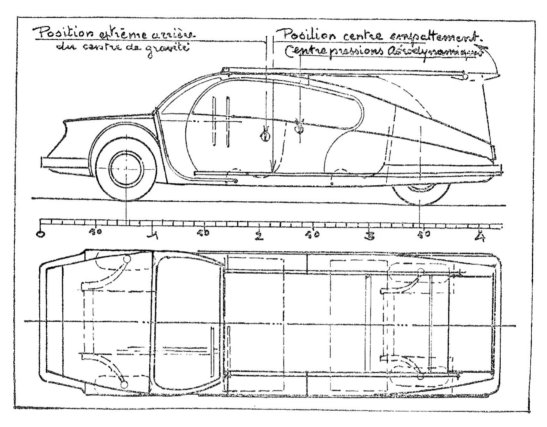

Now consider another of the many possible types of transport: the four-seater grand touring car. This can weigh as little as 500 kilos unladen. It can only be constructed from light alloy, and its engine should be a 1-litre two-stroke to remain within the 5CV fiscal limit. This engine (perhaps along the lines of the German DKW unit) can easily generate 65bhp per litre, and therefore yielding 65-70bhp at 5,000rpm in this application.

This sketch illustrates a car 4.2 metres long and 1.3 metres wide, with a ROOF HEIGHT OF ONLY 1.15 METRES.

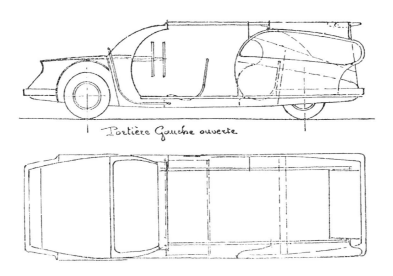

Portière Gauche ouverte

With this very small frontal area and an acceptably aerodynamic shape, it is reasonable to assume that this one-litre four-seater would have a top speed of some 150kph. The presence of two parallel empennages allows the engine to be positioned either at the front or the rear with equal safety. The centre of gravity is 600mm from the ground, a feat difficult to achieve in a touring car. The suspension is fully independent, with only one principal articulation per wheel.

It may be objected that a 2.7 metre wheelbase makes it difficult to achieve a small turning circle, but this can be overcome by the simple expedient of making the rear wheels steerable as well as the front, with two steering wheels placed concentrically one in front of the other. Although this well known arrangement is probably uncommon on road cars for technical and economic reasons, it does allow extraordinary manoeuvrability. The car can, for example, move diagonally, and it greatly simplifies parking manoeuvres.

Lastly, an aerodynamic brake is placed between the two empennages, and raised by the initial part of the brake pedal travel. This has a dual purpose: the vertical downward pressure it exerts improves the adhesion of the rear wheels, and the drag it creates at 150kph is equivalent to 50 kilos - a force of nearly 40 horsepower against the direction of forward travel. At 75kph, this surface still absorbs some four horsepower, as the 'interactions' remain very favourable.

That air brakes should not be more widely used on fast touring cars is inexplicable. The question of 'styling' no doubt intervenes yet again in the climate of general ignorance.

Finally, the sketch shows that all four seats are accessible by a single door sliding back along the length of the body to reveal the passenger compartment, and to make access even easier, can easily be configured to carry back a significant portion of the roof.

This car would be difficult to construct on anything less than an industrial basis, but even with relatively small-scale production, it could be made to sell at around 5,000 new francs. It goes without saying that the interior would be purely functional rather than luxurious and that there would be no needless cosmetic adornments anywhere.

The few prototypes I have built along the lines described here function perfectly well, are incredibly safe and robust enough to withstand whatever punishment. They have met with no success whatever in the eyes of the public…

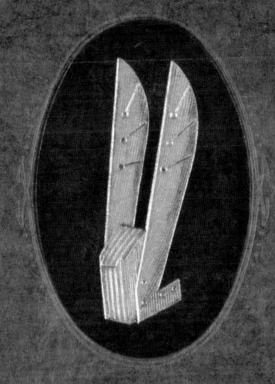

VOISIN

AUTOMOBILES

AVIONS VOISIN

The patents of Gabriel Voisin, 1908-66

1908-11
FR386396   *Flying Fish* monoplane (C&GV)
FR394438   *Aéromobile*
FR401476   Single valve aero engine
FR434696   Elevator wing control

1914-18
FR476887   Reconnaissance sight
FR478008   Aircraft undercarriage
FR524791   Twin-boom airframe
FR524792   Tubular airframe construction
FR524799   Aircraft landing gear
FR478009   Aeroplane (Voisin Type M)
FR491904   Canon mounting
FR492092   Geodesic fuselage construction
FR524812   Aerial machine gun mount
FR524814   Aileron articulation
FR524815   Fuselage member
FR524816   Emergency aileron for triplanes
FR524818   Servo control
FR524820   Twin fuselage canon aeroplane
FR497426   Low-pressure inflatable hangar
FR497506   Servo
FR499285   Carburettor
FR504937   Inflatable mast
FR504975   Inflatable beam

1919
FR500488   Prefabricated housing
FR502149   Sleeve valve lubrication system
FR502150   Headlamp bracket-cum-wing stay
FR503303   Adjustable windscreen mounting
FR503304   Adjustable windscreen mounting
FR503625   Sleeve valve actuation
FR503626   Automobile hood mechanism
FR503627   Automobile scuttle vent
FR503628   Spare wheel mounting
FR504416   Cyclecar gearchange (Sulky)
FR504417   Automobile hood
FR504649   Motorised bicycle wheel (Fly)
FR505470   Clutch
FR505868   Pipe joint

FR506019   Rotating sleeve valve engine
FR507060   Anti-knock spark plug
FR507061   Motorised bicycle wheel (Motor Fly)
FR507210   Pistons and piston rings
FR507269   Variable fuel/air inlet control
FR507270   Heavy duty suspension
FR510539   Aerial stretcher system
FR510699   Air ambulance (Aérochir)

1920
FR510810   Dynastart
FR512224   Cylinder head drainage
FR512225   Clutch or brake pedal system
FR513941   Motorised bicycle transmission
FR517888   Lubrication system
FR525637   Pneumatic braking system
FR526075   V-12 cylinder block
FR526253   Sleeve valve actuation system
FR526436   Compressor wastegate

1921
FR529972   Transverse suspension (C2)
FR538150   Spark analyser
FR540582   Lightweight removable door
FR541766   Engine lubrication system
FR541767   Hydropneumatic braking system
FR541768   Progressive suspension system (C2)
FR545909   Wheel mounting
FR552028   Camshaft for sleeve valve engines
FR552035   Cylinder block (8/10CV)
FR552036   Steering box (8/10CV)

1922
FR546560   Internal engine splash guard
FR538150   Ignition analysis apparatus
FR545794   Door seal
FR545795   Hose clip
FR545908   Coachwork nail
FR545909   Pistons and piston rings
FR545978   Exhausr silencer
FR547100   Hydraulic braking system (C2)
FR547328   Electromagnetic braking system (C2)

FR547649	Steering lubrication
FR458130	Four-wheel brake actuation
FR548822	Engine lubrication
FR548823	Upper sleeve valve lubrication
FR549417	Brake cable
FR550045	Spark plug cooling

1923

FR561546	Gudgeon pin
FR564681	Crankshaft lubrication
FR567721	Lozenge car

1924

FR577104	Steering wheel horn ring
FR578234	Scuttle construction
FR579321	Sliding door glass
FR579655	Pivoting spare wheel/number plate
FR579946	Supercharged high torque engine
FR580774	Obturator
FR581019	Junk head
FR581313	Torque tube
FR582766	Lightweight automobile door lock
FR591876	Remote fuel level gauge

1925

FR592574	Vacuum servo
FR594182	Spare wheel attachment
FR597181	Crankshaft
FR597182	Electric brake servo
FR597493	Engine block
FR597541	Folding door glass
FR597542	Lightweight automobile door
FR599170	Adjustable windscreen
FR599171	Piston rings
FR599209	Automobile door lock
FR599322	Steering damper
FR599474	Folding door glass
FR600327	Dynastart
FR601699	Side luggage boxes
FR603914	Rotary coupling
FR604800	Folding door glass
FR604801	Silent coupling

FR604876	Lightweight body (*Lumineuse*)
FR604986	C-pillar headlight
FR605069	Hydraulic ancillary pump drive
FR606585	Engine lubrication
FR608883	Hood frame (*Lumineuse* Sulky)

1926

FR611980	Hood frame (*Lumineuse* Sulky)
FR613061	Lightweight body construction
FR613420	Hood articulation (Sulky)
FR613584	Engine cooling system
FR614340	Epicyclic transmission
FR617972	Brake balance adjuster
FR617973	Water pump
FR617974	Battery compartment
FR617975	Gearbox casing
FR618094	Cylinder head fixing
FR618254	Gearbox lubrication
FR619017	Balanced brake actuation system

1927

FR622859	Constant velocity joint
FR627596	Auxiliary splash guard
FR627953	Sliding trunnion
FR627954	Side lamp
FR627995	Electrical charging system
FR628451	Brake drum fixing
FR631862	Crankcase
FR633317	Differential
FR634758	Hydraulic/electric relay
FR641998	Pneumatic gear selection system
FR645766	Hydrofoil

1928

FR650224	Lightweight door handle
FR650791	Segmented solid vehicle tyre
FR657237	Automobile cabin ventilation
FR657238	Convertible hood system
FR663746	Battery stowage system
FR663964	Front wheel mounting (FWD V8)
FR663965	Front wheel drive
FR663966	Four wheel steering

FR664209	Starter and dynamo couplings
FR664682	Inboard brake cooling
FR666080	Suspension

1929

FR667603	Underslung suspension
FR668042	V crank configuration
FR668043	V8 sleeve valve engine
FR668653	Gear cutting tool
FR668867	Automobile seat
FR671039	Radiator cap
FR671543	Torque converter
FR672321	Front wheel drive transmission
FR672349	Transmission lubrication
FR672992	Lightweight piston
FR673487	Hydraulic brake system
FR674670	Exhaust silencer
FR675223	Front drive transmission
FR681068	Running board
FR681069	Rotary electrical contact
FR681332	Electromagnetic gearbox
FR681914	Luggage box handles and locks
FR685405	Electromagnetic gearbox
FR686116	Silent gears
FR687142	Rotary electromagnet

1930

FR688692	Cylinder block
FR692374	Wheel disc
FR692992	Constant velocity universal joint

1933-35 (Cie Hellis)

FR748631	Canon
FR752672	Crankshaft
FR768316	Gas safety valve
FR768317	Gas safety valve
FR783051	Engine
FR788412	Retractable roof (Aérodyne)
FR789072	Independent front suspension
FR789073	Electromagnetic clutch
FR791530	Lozenge car
FR799849	Tensioner

1941-46

FR876291	Variable ratio pedal transmission
FR902478	Multi-cylinder pump
FR903657	Steam engine
FR904502	Bimetal piston
FR905126	Seaplane float system
FR905553	Steam engine regulator
FR905554	Steam engine reversing control
FR911385	Bearing
FR911386	Bearing
FR911928	42-cylinder radial aero engine
FR912131	Radial engine connecting rod
FR912755	Pipe bending system
FR912756	Cafetière
FR912757	Aircraft undercarriage
FR920061	Coaxial propeller drive
FR920062	Coaxial propeller drive
FR920063	Tracked aircraft undercarriage
FR937708	Radial engine crankshaft bearing

1952-58

FR1063512	Tracked vehicle
FR1063535	Lightweight high speed tank
FR1084655	Two-stroke engine
FR1085991	Two-stroke engine
FR1146263	Torsion bar suspension
FR1146365	Simplified steering system
FR1146366	Front wheel drive transmission
FR1178878	Oil-cooled cylinder head
FR1178879	Lightweight piston
FR1178880	Roller bearing
FR1189787	Oil-cooled cylinder head
FR1189788	Progressive shock absorber
FR1197890	Small engine cooling system
FR1197891	Simplified steering system

1961-66

FR1312573	Simplified shock absorber
FR1359227	Cream separator
FR1359745	Fluid filter
FR1459257	Failsafe railway locomotive control
FR1497099	Propeller

CH. POST. PARIS 1077-53
RÉF PRODUCTEURS 35.66 SEINE CA

Télégrammes : VOISIN-ISSY

Direction Administration
Approvisionnements
Service Commercial

MICHELET 36-30
REG. DU COM. SEINE 104-885

Aéroplanes G. Voisin

SOCIÉTÉ ANONYME AU CAPITAL DE 30.000.000 DE FRANCS

AUTOMOBILE - AÉRONAUTIQUE - MÉCANIQUE

36, Boulevard Gambetta, Issy-les-Moulineaux

N°.
à rappeler

ISSY-les-MOULINEAUX (Seine), le

Acknowledgements

This edition would not have been possible without the unstinting help and advice of Philippe Ladure, Stefan Ittner, Thierry Auffret, Francis Metzger, Pierre-Michel Aubert and other friends from Les Amis de Gabriel Voisin as well as the encouragement of Jonathan Rishton.

For the many factory photographs reproduced here, I am especially indebted to the generosity of Jacquy Feuillade, to Stefan Ittner and to Jan de Lange for the Salon shots of the Biscooter. The main photograph on p.174 is by kind permission of LAT Photographic, and the other images are reproduced from contemporary publications or from my own and other private collections.

Société Ano des Aéroplanes G. VOISIN
Le Président du Conseil d'Administration
Directeur Général

INDEX

1922 ACF GP, Strasbourg	*145-151*
1923 ACF GP, Tours	*161-165*
1924 ACF GP, Lyon	*172-6*
Aéromécanique	*224-5, 228, 237, 250*
Ariel	*73-77, 123, 215, 217*
Artault, Ernest	*38, 40, 83, 106, 146*
Austin Mini	*121*
Aviation Construction Service	*12, 14*
Ballet Russes	*246-7*
Barbezat, Maurice	*166*
Benzole	*184, 188-90*
Bernard, Marius	*119, 121-5, 128, 133, 137, 163, 180-1, 185, 191, 207, 224, 231, 234, 237, 258*
Birkigt, Marc	*105*
Bloch, Edmond	*29*
Blue Train	*107, 121*
Bourguin, Paul	*237*
Brangues	*226*
Bugatti, Ettore	*27, 106, 165, 237, 242*
Cannes	*23, 37, 69-70, 77, 101, 123*
Capo di Monte	*23, 37*
Casanova, Damián	*243-6, 249*
Châlons-sur-Saône	*69, 225*
Champ de manoeuvres	*11, 46*
Chantier Naval Voisin	*217-8, 244*
Chausson	*183*
Chevrolet	*177*
Christian belief	*96-7*
Chrysler	*195-7, 207*
Circuit des Routes Pavées	*151-3, 173, 208*
Citroën, André	*25, 40, 51, 143, 209, 211*
Citroën 2CV	*31, 241, 249, 255, 280*
Claudel, Paul	*24, 225-6*
Cornuché, Gustave	*38, 56*
Cotal	*111, 119, 135*
Côte de Limonest	*83*
Cozette, René	*179*
Cugnot	*47, 195, 211*
Damazzio	*55*
Daninos, Pierre	*257*
Danilova, Alexandra	*246-7*
de Bougainville, Louis	*51-2*
Decarme, Albert	*34, 43, 103, 152*
de Gaulle, Charles	*233-4*
Desbruères, Henri	*239*
Djalini, Sylvia	*98-101, 142-3*
DKW	*284*
Dufresne, Louis	*40, 119, 146*
Dufour	*183*
Duray, Arthur	*149, 151, 165*
Esmée	*57, 59, 61, 95, 97-9, 141-2, 225, 227, 229-30*
Exelmans (Blvd)	*31, 37, 41, 55-7, 59, 99, 172, 207-8, 212, 219, 221, 224-5, 229-31, 239, 243, 250, 258*
Farman, Henry	*259*
Faroux, Charles	*151*
Ferreri, Gabriel	*250*
Fouillaron	*65*
Ford, Henry	*25*
Foudre	*20-21*
France, Anatole	*9*
Franco (General)	*244, 246*
Gaillon hillclimb	*83, 92*
Gaston Williams Wigmore	*55*
Gaudermann, Richard	*83, 149, 151, 172, 175-6*
Gaumont, Louis	*152*
Gille, Victor	*41*
Gnome & Rhône	*20, 224-6, 233, 237, 239, 243-5*
Graham Paige	*222-3*
Héreil, Georges	*207*
Hispano Suiza	*14, 16, 27, 46, 81, 83, 105, 224, 245*
Iribe, Paul	*41*
Kapferer, Henry	*154-5, 169, 215*
Kellner	*79*
Kiriloff, Serge	*189*
Knight engine	*30, 38, 40-3, 115-9, 124, 147, 211*
Latil	*91*
L'Angelo	*142, 215, 227, 229-30*
La Cadolle	*212-3*
La Darse	*218*
Le Talus	*77*

Laboratoire   15, 17, 69-70, 80, 157, 165, 181, 197, 199, 219
Lafay, Colonel   168
Lamberjack, Dominique   106-7, 151, 156
Lefebvre, André   15, 70, 133, 137, 163, 165, 173, 181,
                                       191, 208-9, 211, 241, 257
Lefebvre, Charles   14, 15, 21, 23, 40
Lepicard, Jean   237
Lockheed   49
Lorraine Dietrich   28-30, 93, 209

Maisons Voisin   31-33
Margueritte, Victor   56, 77
Maxim's   38, 55-7, 99
Mazoyer   87, 89, 133
Menier, Antoine   193
Mercedes   30, 193
Métallurgique   30
Moglia, Edmond   242-3
Mont Ventoux   55, 83, 166, 173
Montlhéry Autodrome   176-9, 188, 191, 195-7
Morane, Léon   36
Morel, André   165, 173, 175-6

Noël Telmont, André-Noël   31,73, 219
Notre-Dame-de-la-Garde   101-3
Nuclear energy   72, 251

Packard   166-7, 222
Panhard   9, 30, 38, 40, 111, 115, 119, 251
Patout, Pierre   31
Pegamoid   111
Peretti, Serge   140
Perrichon, Georges   250
Peugeot   27, 46, 119, 146, 149, 151, 153, 165, 176
Piat   33, 83
Piganeau   49
Pleven, René   235
Potez, Henry   241

Quai du Point du Jour   28-9, 34

Renault, Louis   143, 152/3, 208/9
Rochet-Schneider   29
Rolls Royce   71, 111, 167, 200-1
Rougier, Henri   28, 83,93, 149, 165, 172, 175
Serpollet   27

Simca   207, 267
SNECMA   233-243, 258-9
Stanley   27
Stephenson, George   275-6

Tabuteau, Maurice   111-3
Thiroloix, Jules-Alexandre   16

Van Roggen, Mathieu   204-5, 208, 223
Vélosolex   146
Viallet, Fernand   15, 228
Viard, Captain   250
Villefranche-sur-Mer   217-9, 260
Villiers   244-5
Voisin, Charles (brother)   27, 38, 48
Voisin, Charles (nephew)   235
Voisin, Janine   24-5
Voisin automobiles
   Aérosport   19, 193, 195, 202, 250
   Biscooter/Biscuter   93-4, 119, 237-249
   Prototype   40, 42-7
   C1 (18CV)   50-1, 54-5, 60, 80, 82, 107
   C2 (40CV)   49, 66-71
   C3/C3L (18CV)   112, 114, 126-7, 130, 144, 146, 155
   C4/C7 (8/10CV) 71, 110, 118-9, 120-1, 125, 151-3, 208
   C5 (18CV)   84-93, 105
   C6 *Laboratoire*   161-165
   C11/14 (13CV)   71, 122-6,134-7, 163, 203
   C12 (24CV)   158
   C16 (33CV)   157-9
   C20 V12 (28CV)   195, 198-9, 201, 208
   C23/24/25 (17CV)   187, 193
   C30   119, 222-4
   FWD V8   203, 208, 237
   Lozenge car   219-221
   Sleeve valve radial   221
   Steam engines and cars   62-3, 71, 229-30, 251
   TEP   251-3

Weiller, Paul-Louis   224-6, 235
Weyher et Richemond   27
Weymann, Charles   110-3

Yacco   183, 187

293

Eugène Gabriel Voisin
(1880-1973)